M000206949

ABBREVIATIONS FOR CHAPTER TITLES

When your instructor uses one of these abbreviations in marking your paper, you should read or review all the material in the designated chapter.

James A. W. Heffernan

Dartmouth College

John E. Lincoln

WRITING

A COLLEGE WORKBOOK

W. W. NORTON & COMPANY
NEW YORK   LONDON

Copyright © 1982 by W. W. Norton & Company, Inc.
Published simultaneously in Canada by George J. McLeod Limited, Toronto.
Printed in the United States of America
All Rights Reserved
First Edition

Gwendolyn Brooks: First stanza from "a song in the front yard" (p. 12) in *The World of Gwendolyn Brooks* by Gwendolyn Brooks. Copyright 1945 by Gwendolyn Brooks Blakely. Reprinted by permission of Harper & Row, Publishers, Inc.
Henry Gleitman: from *Psychology* by Henry Gleitman. Copyright ©1981 by W. W. Norton & Company, Inc. Reprinted by permission of W. W. Norton & Company, Inc.
Conrad Kent Rivers: from "The Still Voice of Harlem." In *The Still Voice of Harlem,* London, Paul Breman Ltd., 1968. Reprinted by permission.

W. W. Norton & Company, Inc. 500 Fifth Avenue, New York, N.Y. 10110
W. W. Norton & Company Ltd. 37 Great Russell Street, London WC1B 3NU

ISBN 0 393 95177 4

1 2 3 4 5 6 7 8 9 0

PREFACE

Writing—A College Workbook is a basic textbook on the writing of sentences. It is designed as a supplement to *Writing—A College Handbook,* but it may also be used by itself or with other books in a writing course.

While the *Handbook* explains the writing process as a whole, the *Workbook* focuses on the writing of sentences because problems with sentence structure often constitute the biggest hurdle student writers have to overcome. The *Workbook* follows the *Handbook* in its basic approach to sentence structure, and the explanatory terms used in both books are essentially the same. But the instructions in the *Workbook* are more elementary, and the exercises are in general simpler, asking frequently for the recognition of sentence elements and the correction of difficulties most commonly found in student writing. At the same time, the *Workbook* also includes a number of sentence-combining exercises, and these are designed to let students see the variety of effects they can generate with a variety of constructions. Thus the *Workbook* reinforces the fundamentally positive thrust of the *Handbook,* reasserting the point that good writing is not simply the absence of grammatical error, but the presence of rhetorical power.

Each chapter and section of the *Workbook* corresponds to a chapter or section in Part II of the *Handbook,* "Writing Sentences." For example, chapter 2 in the *Workbook,* "Modifiers," corresponds to a chapter with the same title in the *Handbook*—chapter 11. Likewise, section 2.11 in the *Workbook,* "Misplaced Modifiers," corresponds to a section with the same title in the *Handbook*—section 11.11. As a result, students using the *Handbook* can readily find in the *Workbook* further instruction and further exercises on all of the major topics treated in Part II of the *Handbook.* Alternatively, students can use the chapters or sections of the *Workbook* as preparation for the corresponding chapters or sections of the *Handbook.*

But since the *Workbook* is a systematic and self-contained guide to the writing of sentences, it can also be used by itself. No part of the *Workbook* presupposes a knowledge of the *Handbook;* instructional parts of the *Workbook* give all the information necessary for completion of the exercises. All the exercises are printed on separate pages, which can be torn out and handed in to the instructor while the rest of the book remains intact for future reference.

Answers to the exercises in this book can be found in the instructor's manual. The answers are also available in a separate pamphlet, for use by students at the instructor's option.

We wish to thank Ann Page Stecker and Nancy Heffernan, who helped us considerably in the preparation of these exercises, and also Debbie Hodges, who did a first-class job of typing the entire manuscript.

James A. W. Heffernan
John E. Lincoln

Note: Nonstandard constructions in this book are marked with a star (*) except in chapter 8, "Complete Sentences and Sentence Fragments," where sentence fragments are not starred because they are acceptable under certain special circumstances.

CONTENTS

1

THE SIMPLE SENTENCE— SUBJECT AND PREDICATE

1.1 The Subject and the Predicate

A sentence is a group of words consisting of a subject and a predicate. The **subject** is the word or word group that tells who or what the sentence is about. The **predicate** is the word or word group that tells what the subject does, has, or is, or what is done to it:

SUBJECT	PREDICATE
Mosquitoes	bite.
Karen	kicked the ball.
Jogging	is popular.
The first president	was George Washington.
Lincoln	was shot.
The apartment	has wall-to-wall carpeting.

1.2 The Sentence and the Clause

Every sentence normally has at least one subject and one predicate; the combination of the two is called a **clause**. A sentence may have more than one clause:

    S   P   S   P
    Bob / painted the fence, and Sally / weeded the garden.

    S   P   S   P
    I / knocked loudly, but no one / answered the door.

In later chapters we consider sentences such as these—sentences with two or more clauses. In this chapter we treat the one-clause sentence, usually called the **simple sentence**.

1.3 About the Predicate

Verbs and Verb Phrases

The verb in a sentence is one of three types: transitive, intransitive, or linking.

A **transitive verb** names an action that directly affects a person or thing named in the predicate. The word or word group naming this person or thing is the direct object of the verb. In each of the following sentences the direct object comes right after the verb (shown in italics):

> I *saw* David.
> The snowball *broke* the window.
> Paper planes *filled* the air.

An **intransitive verb** names an action that has no direct impact on anyone or anything named in the predicate:

> Sinatra *frowned.*
> Sap *runs* in the spring.

A **linking verb** (often a form of *be,* such as *is, are, was,* or *were*) is followed by a word or phrase that identifies or describes the subject:

> The capital of North Dakota *is* Bismarck.
> In 1981 Ronald Reagan *became* president.
> The natives *seemed* friendly.
> Ralph *looked* eager.

Linking verbs include *seem, become, feel, look, sound,* and *taste,* as well as *be*—the most common of all.

A word that follows a linking verb and identifies the subject is called a **predicate noun.** In the preceding examples *Bismarck* and *president* are predicate nouns. A word that follows a linking verb and describes the subject is called a **predicate adjective.** In the preceding examples *friendly* and *eager* are predicate adjectives.

A **verb phrase** consists of two or more verbs—a base verb and at least one "helping" verb, usually called an **auxiliary**:

SUBJECT	PREDICATE	
	ONE OR MORE AUXILIARIES	BASE VERB
Frank	could	leave.
Frank	could have	left.
Work	has	started.
The building	will be	finished.

Besides *could, have, has, will,* and *be,* auxiliaries include *is, are, was, were, been, had, may, might, must, shall, do, does, did, would,* and *should.*

Normally the predicate follows the subject, but in many questions the sentence begins with an auxiliary:

PREDICATE	SUBJECT	PREDICATE
Could	Frank	leave?
Could	Frank	have left?
Has	work	started?
Will	the building	be finished?

Voice—Active and Passive

A transitive verb can be written in either the active or the passive voice. A verb is in the **active voice** when the subject performs the action named by the verb:

Beavers *build* dams.

A verb is in the **passive voice** when the subject undergoes the action named by the verb:

Dams *are built* by beavers.

The performer of the action can be specified in a *by* phrase after the verb. But the performer is not always specified:

A shot *was fired.*

(For a full discussion of the active and passive voice, see chapter 13, pp. 203–10.)

Objects—Direct and Indirect

A transitive verb can have two objects: a direct object, as already shown, and an indirect object. The **direct object** names the person or thing directly affected by the action that the verb specifies:

Fiona plays *the guitar.*
Rusty gave *a party.*

The **indirect object** names the person or thing indirectly affected by the action that the verb specifies:

Rusty gave a party for *Samantha.*
I showed the bill to *my father.*
The owner offered *me* a job.

The indirect object may go after the direct object or immediately after the verb. When it goes immediately after a verb like *send, give, show, offer, write,* or *told,* it can be used without *to* or *for.*

Object Complements

An **object complement** is a word or word group that immediately follows a direct object and identifies or describes it:

Ellen found the gas tank *empty.*
We made Rosenberg *our spokesman.*

Object complements follow such verbs as *name, elect, appoint, think, consider, judge, find* (in the sense of "judge"), and *make.*

1.4 About the Subject— Nouns, Pronouns, Verbal Nouns, and Noun Phrases

The subject of a sentence can be a single **noun**, a word that names a person, creature, place, thing, activity, condition, or idea:

> *Mosquitoes* hummed.
> *Jack* threw the ball.
> *Austin* is the capital of Texas.
> *Terrorism* must be stopped.

The subject can also be a single **pronoun**, a word that takes the place of a noun:

> *I* studied the map.
> *We* had taken the wrong road.

(For a full discussion of pronouns, see chapter 9, pp. 141-58.)
Sometimes the subject is a **verbal noun**, a word or phrase that is formed from a verb and used as a noun:

> *Surfing* takes practice.
> *To work* is to pray.

(For a full discussion of verbal nouns, see chapter 3, pp. 59-68.)
Frequently the subject is a **noun phrase**, a group of words consisting of a noun and its modifiers—the words that describe, limit, or qualify it:

> *The tiger* stirred.
> *The hungry lion* roared.
> *The loud rumble of a jeep* awakened me.

In each of these sentences the complete subject consists of the base subject and its modifiers. The base subjects are *tiger, lion,* and *rumble.*

1.5 Modifiers

As just stated, a **modifier** is a word or phrase that describes, limits, or qualifies another word or phrase in a sentence:

> *The hungry* lion roared.
> *The* unicorn is *a mythical* beast.
> The room was *insufferably* hot.
> Banners fluttered *in the breeze.*
> Marian could have won *easily.*

The word or phrase modified may be a base subject (*lion*), a predicate noun (*beast*), a predicate adjective (*hot*), a verb (*fluttered*), or a verb phrase (*could have won*). Since modifiers include even such words as *the* and *a*, nearly all sentences have at least one, and most sentences have them in both the subject and the predicate. In the following examples the modifiers are italicized:

SUBJECT	PREDICATE
The banners	fluttered *gaily.*
The colored banners	fluttered *gaily in the breeze.*
The brightly colored banners	fluttered *gaily in the early morning breeze.*
Waving on high, the brightly colored banners	fluttered *gaily in the early morning breeze.*
Ronald Reagan	became *the president in 1981.*
Ronald Reagan	became *the president of the United States in 1981.*
Ralph	looked *eager.*
Ralph	looked *eager for a fight.*
Clenching his fists, Ralph	looked *eager for a fight.*

(For a full discussion of modifiers, see chapter 2, pp. 19–58.)

1.6   Compounds

A **compound phrase** is a word group consisting of two or more nouns, verbs, or modifiers joined by a connecting word such as *and:*

Joan, Steve, Sally, and I went to the party.
We *danced and sang* until 2:00 A.M.
The band was *hot, electric, and deafening.*
At 2:00 A.M. the *happy but exhausted* crowd dispersed.

(For more on compound phrases, see section 4.2, pp. 69–70.)

Name _____ Date _____

Exercise 1.   Recognizing and Using Subjects and Predicates

Part A.   In each of the following sentences, separate the subject and predicate with a slash, and identify the subject (*S*) and the predicate (*P*). Then write a new sentence that follows the form of the original.

EXAMPLE
S   P
Jack / pounded the door.

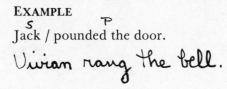

Vivian rang the bell.

1.   The flowers withered.

2.   Hecklers jeered the speech.

3.   Nuclear power is controversial.

4.   The whale is a mammal.

5.   Barbara was stung.

6.   The dog leaped the fence.

7.   I felt a drop of rain on my nose.

8.   An iron fence surrounded the house.

9.   The door was locked.

10.   I had no key.

Part B. In each of the following sentences, separate the subject and predicate with a slash, identify the subject (*S*) and the predicate (*P*), and underline the auxiliary or auxiliaries in the verb phrase. Then write a new sentence that follows the form of the original, using the same auxiliary or auxiliaries.

EXAMPLE

$\overset{S}{\text{The city}} / \overset{P}{\underline{\text{must be}}\ \text{revitalized.}}$

The school must be expanded.

1. The dam might burst.

2. Karen should have been chosen.

3. The little girl did complete the marathon.

4. The deer had scented the hunters.

5. The battle can be won.

6. I could have seen the whole game.

7. I will take chemistry next semester.

8. Does the moon have an atmosphere?

9. We must stop the arms race.

10. Republicans are savoring their victories.

Name _____ Date _____

Exercise 2. Recognizing and Using Transitive and Intransitive Verbs

Part A. Each of the following sentences contains a verb that is either transitive or intransitive. If the verb is intransitive, circle it; if the verb is transitive, underline it and draw an arrow to its direct object.

EXAMPLES

Banners (fluttered) in the early morning breeze.

A savage tornado <u>devastated</u> the town.

1. Peter jumped.

2. The Shakers invented the clothespin.

3. Leaves fell.

4. Sharon develops her own pictures.

5. The hunter studied the trail carefully.

6. Jill spoke in a hoarse whisper.

7. The dog barked.

8. A hitchhiker stood in the middle of the road.

9. Sal hit the brakes.

10. The brakes failed.

Part B. Use each of the following verbs in two simple sentences. Make the verb intransitive in the first sentence and transitive in the second, and underline the direct object of the verb in the second.

EXAMPLE

whispered

Pete whispered.

Pete whispered <u>the answer</u>.

1. sang

2. whistled

3. played

4. pitched

5. shook

6. ate

7. kicked

8. froze

9. stretched

10. drove

Name _____ Date _____

Exercise 3. Recognizing Linking Verbs, Predicate Nouns, and Predicate Adjectives

Part A. In each of the following sentences, circle the linking verb. Then underline the predicate noun and any modifiers it may have.

EXAMPLES

Whales (are) mammals.

Whales (are) large mammals.

1. Spying is a risky occupation.

2. Our vacation was a disaster.

3. On the death of John F. Kennedy, Lyndon Johnson became president of the United States.

4. My favorite sport is hockey.

5. Hunting is a controversial sport.

6. A carnivore is a meat eater.

7. The Vikings may have been the first European visitors to North America.

8. In spite of major growth nearby, Patonia remains a small town.

9. Francis Davis was the inventor of power steering.

10. The setting sun was a bloodshot eye winking over the horizon.

Part B. In each of the following sentences, circle the linking verb. Then underline the predicate adjective and any modifiers it may have.

EXAMPLE

The novel (was) long.

1. Jack felt nervous.

2. Hang gliding is dangerous.

3. The baby stayed quiet.

4. The president sounded a little anxious.

5. Andrew seemed restless.

6. The party was unbearably dull.

7. The pizza tasted strange.

8. Felicia acted suspicious of everyone.

9. The house looked empty.

10. After a long day on the trail, we were hungry.

Name _____ Date _____

Exercise 4. Recognizing Direct Objects, Indirect Objects, and Object Complements

Part A. In each of the following sentences, circle the verb. Then underline the direct object once and the indirect object twice.

EXAMPLE

My father (bought) me a motorcycle.

1. The lifeguard gave them a sharp warning.

2. I sent my application to the main office.

3. The real-estate agent showed us a three-bedroom house.

4. The congressman sent a letter to his constituents.

5. A few weeks ago, everyone in our civics class wrote a letter to the president.

6. On the first day of class the teacher told us the story of her life.

7. The dealer offered me a five-hundred-dollar trade-in allowance.

8. I bought a pair of gloves for my brother.

9. He made a night table for me.

10. Every year I send Christmas cards to all of my relatives.

Part B. In each of the following sentences, circle the verb. Then underline the direct object once and the object complement twice.

EXAMPLE

We (found) the trail poorly marked and overgrown.

1. The new mayor appointed her husband park commissioner.

2. What makes some players stars?

3. Many voters consider inflation the biggest problem of all.

4. I found her argument unconvincing.

5. She thought me unreasonable.

6. U.S. voters elected Franklin Delano Roosevelt president four times in a row.

7. The court judged Rollins sane and competent to stand trial.

8. The delay made me angry.

9. Many musicians consider Jascha Heifetz the greatest violinist of his time.

10. Shortly after his election to the presidency, Ronald Reagan named Alexander Haig secretary of state.

1.7   Faulty Predication   *pred*

Faulty predication is the use of a linking verb between two expressions that are not equivalent. Consider this example:

> *One way to start a speech is a story.

This sentence tries to say that an action is equivalent to a story. But an action and a story are not equivalent. To correct the sentence, you must make the story part of an action:

> One way to start a speech is to tell a story.

Here is another example:

> *Spelunking is when you explore caves.

This sentence tries to say that spelunking is equivalent to a particular time—a *when*. But spelunking is not a particular time; it is an activity that may occur at different times. To correct the sentence, use a term that specifies an activity:

> Spelunking is cave exploring.

Here is one more example:

> *The reason for the protest march was because wreckers had come to demolish the church.

This sentence tries to say that a *reason* is *because*. Those two words seem to go together, but they are not equivalent; *reason* is a noun, and *because* is not. To correct the sentence, use *that* instead of *because:*

> The reason for the protest march was that wreckers had come to demolish the church.

That wreckers had come to demolish the church is a noun clause, the equivalent of a noun. (For more on noun clauses, see section 6.3, p. 100.)

Name ———————————————————— Date ————————————————

Exercise 5. Recognizing and Using Correct Predication

Part A.   Each of the following consists of two sentences with linking verbs. In one sentence the predication is correct; in the other it is faulty. Circle the letter of the sentence with correct predication.

> EXAMPLE
>
> (a)   Abdication is when someone renounces a throne or high office.
>
> ((b))   Abdication is renunciation of a throne or high office.

1. (a)   One way to demonstrate your ability is when you take a test.
    (b)   One way to demonstrate your ability is to take a test.

2. (a)   The chief reason for the decline of cities is because many middle-class families have moved to the suburbs.
    (b)   The chief reason for the decline of cities is that many middle-class families have moved to the suburbs.

3. (a)   Directing a play is where you make individual performers work together.
    (b)   Directing a play is a process of making individual performers work together.

4. (a)   The main problem with battery-powered cars at present is how you have to recharge them about once every hundred miles.
    (b)   The main problem with battery-powered cars at present is their need for recharging about once every hundred miles.

5. (a)   One of David's great achievements was hitting Goliath with the stone.
    (b)   One of David's great achievements was when he hit Goliath with the stone.

Part B. Each of the following consists of one whole sentence and the first part of another. Complete the second sentence with a phrase like the one italicized in the first.

EXAMPLE

Activity is *the only road to knowledge.* —George Bernard Shaw

Negligence is the quickest route to failure.

1. The main disadvantage of the site was *its bumpy terrain.*

   The main advantage of the site was _____

   _____

2. New York City is *a concrete jungle.*

   The United States is _____

   _____

3. The rainbow has lately become *a cult symbol.*

   The Goodyear blimp has lately become_____

   _____

4. The anthropologist's main interest is *studying man's social and cultural behavior.*

   The adman's principal interest is _____

   _____

5. His obsession is *to follow in his father's footsteps.*

   Her goal is _____

   _____

2

MODIFIERS

2.1 What Modifiers Do

A **modifier** is a word or word group that describes, limits, or qualifies another word or word group in a sentence. Modifiers include adjectives, adverbs, participles, infinitives, appositives, and absolute phrases.

2.2 Adjectives and Adjective Phrases

Adjectives

An **adjective** is a word that modifies a noun by telling such things as how many, what kind, and which one:

The *heavy* boots of the *three old* men sank into the *sticky* mud

of the *narrow* trail.

As noted earlier (p. 2), an adjective that modifies the subject can appear in the predicate, and it is then called a predicate adjective:

[S] The tent / [P] was *green.*

[S] Sharks / [P] are *ruthless.*

Misusing Adjectives

Do not use an adjective to modify a verb or verb phrase:

*For the first part of the trip, the old Chevy ran good.

Good is an adjective, but it is here used to modify a verb, *ran.* It should be replaced by the adverb *well:*

For the first part of the trip, the old Chevy ran well.

Here is another example:

> *The policeman looked at me suspicious.

Suspicious is an adjective, but it is here used to modify a verb, *looked.* It should be replaced by the adverb *suspiciously:*

> The policeman looked at me suspiciously. [or] The policeman looked suspiciously at me.

Adjective Phrases

An **adjective phrase** is a word group that modifies a noun:

> I bought a clock *with a luminous dial.*

> A girl *in a raincoat* gave me directions.

A phrase that starts with a preposition—a word like *with, under, by, of,* or *at*—is called a **prepositional phrase.** Phrases of this type are often used to modify nouns.

The nouns in an adjective phrase can be modified by adjectives and other adjective phrases:

> I bought a clock with a *luminous* dial.

> A girl in a *black* raincoat gave me directions to the *new* airport.

And like a single adjective, an adjective phrase that modifies the subject of a sentence can appear in the predicate after a linking verb:

> [S] The sheriff / [P] was *in a hurry.*

2.3 Nouns in Place of Adjectives

A noun used before another noun often serves as an adjective. Like an adjective, it modifies the word that comes next:

> The *winter* wind cut through me like a knife.

> Fish goes well with *lemon* juice.

> *Football* practice took a lot of my time.

Do not overuse nouns as adjectives. If you do, your sentence may be confusing:

> I couldn't find the amplifier kit instruction manual parts list.

To clarify a sentence like this, turn some of the nouns into ordinary adjectives or adjective phrases:

> I couldn't find the list of parts in the instructional manual for the amplifier kit.

2.4   Adverbs and Adverb Phrases

Adverbs

An **adverb** is a word that tells such things as how, when, where, and why. It modifies a verb, an adjective, another adverb, or a whole clause. Most adverbs are formed by the addition of *-ly* to the adjective.

1. Modifying a verb:

> The engines failed *suddenly*.

2. Modifying an adjective:

> The pilot was *surprisingly* calm.

3. Modifying another adverb:

> He handled the plane *remarkably* well.

4. Modifying a whole clause:

> *Fortunately,* no one was injured.

Misusing Adverbs

Do not use an adverb to modify a noun:

> *By noon the sky had become darkly.

Darkly is an adverb, but it is here used to modify a noun, *sky.* It should be replaced by the adjective *dark:*

> By noon the sky had become dark.

Adverb Phrases

An **adverb phrase** is a word group that modifies a verb, an adjective, an adverb, or a whole clause.

1. Modifying a verb:

> Bob runs *like a jackrabbit.*

2. Modifying an adjective:

> Big *in the shoulders,* Vic nearly split the seams of the jacket.

3. Modifying an adverb:

> *Not at all* eagerly, she agreed.

4. Modifying a whole clause:

> *In an emergency,* a flight attendant can give first aid.

The words *like, to, at,* and *in* are prepositions, so the phrases they introduce are prepositional phrases. As noted on p. 20, a prepositional phrase can be used as an adjective; it can also be used as an adverb. Indeed, the same group of words can be an adjective phrase in one sentence and an adverb phrase in another:

The view *from the balcony* was spectacular.

The crazed man jumped *from the balcony*.

In the first sentence, *from the balcony* is an adjective phrase modifying the noun *view*. In the second sentence, *from the balcony* is an adverb phrase modifying the verb *jumped*.

2.5 Comparatives and Superlatives

The comparative and the superlative are forms of the adjective and the adverb. The **comparative** is used to compare one thing with another; the **superlative** is used to compare one thing with all others in a group of three or more.

The Comparative Forms of Adjectives

You make most adjectives comparative by adding *-er* to them: *short, shorter; tall, taller; mighty, mightier.* A comparative adjective starts a comparison between two different things or sets of things. If the adjective is a long word, you use *more* before it instead of adding *-er; more dangerous, more beautiful.* You use *less* before an adjective of any length: *less tall, less dangerous, less beautiful.* (Important exceptions are *good,* whose comparative is *better,* and *bad,* whose comparative is *worse.* See "Special Forms," p. 24.)

A comparative adjective must normally be followed by *than* plus a noun:

The pen is mightier than the sword.
Cats are more devious than dogs.
Flying is often less dangerous than driving.

The Comparative Forms of Adverbs

You make adverbs ending in *-ly* comparative by using *more* before them: *more noisily, more carefully.* If the adverb does not end in *-ly,* you add *-er: faster.* You use *less* before an adverb whatever its ending: *less carefully.* A comparative adverb is normally followed by *than* plus the rest of a phrase that makes the meaning clear:

Charlie sang more noisily than anyone else at the party.
We could drive faster on the new interstate than on the old three-lane highway.
Many products can be made abroad less expensively than in the United States.

Misusing Comparatives

Do not use *more* and *-er* together, as in *more smarter or **more closer.*

Do not leave a comparison unfinished:

> Gasohol is cheaper.

Gasohol is cheaper than what? The writer should complete the comparison:

> Gasohol is cheaper than gas.

The Superlative Forms of Adjectives

You make most adjectives superlative by adding *-est* to them: *strong, strongest.* If the adjective is a long word, you use *most* before it instead of adding *-est: most competent.* You use *least* before an adjective of any length: *least efficient.* (Important exceptions are *good* and *bad;* their superlatives are *best* and *worst,* not **goodest* and **baddest.* See "Special Forms," p. 24.)

Since the superlative adjective is normally used to compare one thing with all others in a group, the group should be clearly identified:

> Wendy is the fastest player on the team.
> Beating is the least effective way to teach a child anything.

In these sentences, Wendy is compared with all other players on the team, and beating is compared with all other ways of teaching a child.

The Superlative Forms of Adverbs

You make adverbs ending in *-ly* superlative by using *most* before them: *most carefully.* If the adverb does not end in *-ly,* you add *-est: closest, fastest.* You use *least* before an adverb whatever its ending: *least close, least carefully.* Like a sentence with a superlative adjective, a sentence with a superlative adverb should normally identify the group with which the comparison is being made:

> *Star Wars* may be the most successfully promoted movie of all time.
> Of all the old western gunslingers, Jesse James shot fastest.

In these sentences, *Star Wars* is compared with all other movies, and Jesse James is compared with all other old western gunslingers.

Misusing Superlatives

Do not use most and *-est* together, as in **most closest* or **most fastest.*

Do not use the superlative without identifying the group of persons or things involved in the comparison:

> Patton was the boldest.

Patton was the boldest of what? The writer should identify a group:

> Of all the U.S. Army generals in World War II, Patton was the boldest.

Special Forms

As noted earlier, some modifiers have special forms for the comparative and superlative:

POSITIVE	COMPARATIVE	SUPERLATIVE
good [adjective] } well [adverb] }	better	best
bad [adjective] } badly [adverb] }	worse	worst
little [adjective and adverb, for quantity]	less	least
much [adjective and adverb]	more	most
far [adjective and adverb]	farther	farthest

2.6 Participles and Participle Phrases

Participles

A **participle** is a word normally made by the addition of *-ing, -d,* or *-ed* to the bare form (present tense) of a verb. Participles are often used as modifiers. Consider these sentences:

> *Whistling,* she walked out of the room.
> The *whistling* girl walked out of the room.
> She walked out of the room *whistling.*

> *Stunned,* he walked out of the conference.
> The *stunned* governor walked out of the conference.
> He walked out of the conference *stunned.*

The addition of *-ing* to the verb makes a **present participle**; the addition of *-d* or *-ed* makes a **past participle**.

Participle Phrases

A **participle phrase** consists of a participle, any modifiers it may have, and sometimes an object. Like a participle, a participle phrase modifies a noun or pronoun:

> *Softly whistling,* the girl left the room.

The adverb *Softly* modifies the participle *whistling.* In turn, the participle phrase modifies *the girl.*

Like a verb, a participle can have an object:

> *Softly whistling a cheerful tune,* she left the room.

A cheerful tune is the object of the participle *whistling.* The participle phrase modifies *she.*

Here are further examples of participle phrases:

> *Stunned by the accusation*, the governor walked out of the conference.

The phrase modifies *the governor*.

> *Leaving a trail of cookie crumbs*, Jenny slowly climbed the stairs.

The phrase modifies *Jenny*.

> The lookout stays alert, *carefully scanning the horizon for traces of other ships*.

The phrase modifies *The lookout*.

2.7 Infinitives and Infinitive Phrases

Infinitives

An **infinitive** is a form usually made by the placing of **to** before the bare form (present tense) of a verb. Infinitives are often used as modifiers:

> Ferguson is playing *to win*.
>
> Eager *to start*, the horse champed at the bit.
>
> Pressed *to sing*, I croaked out a few bars of "My Old Kentucky Home."
>
> Guns feed the desire *to kill*.

Infinitives occasionally include *be, have, or have been;* these infinitives are made with the past participle: *to be elected, to be feared, to have danced, to have been chosen.* (For more on infinitives of this type, see section 11.4, p. 182.)

Infinitive Phrases

An **infinitive phrase** consists of an infinitive, any modifiers it may have, and sometimes an object:

> Eager *to start at once*, the horse champed at the bit.

At once modifies the infinitive *to start*. In turn, the infinitive phrase modifies *Eager*.

> It was a noise *to wake the dead*.

The dead is the object of the infinitive *to wake*. The infinitive phrase modifies *a noise*.

> *In order to win the election decisively*, he needed the votes of the California delegation.

Here the infinitive phrase expresses purpose and modifies a whole clause, *he needed the votes of the California delegation.* You can emphasize purpose by putting *in order* before the infinitive.

Split Infinitives

In general, you should avoid splitting the infinitive—that is, putting one or more words between *to* and the bare form of the verb:

> WEAK: Her main job as a labor mediator is *to effectively settle* disputes.
> REVISED: Her main job as a labor mediator is *to settle* disputes effectively.

Split an infinitive only with a modifier that might be awkward in any other position:

> You must spend many years in Southeast Asia *to fully understand* the problems faced by people living there.

2.8 Appositives

An **appositive** is a noun or noun phrase that is used to describe or identify another noun or noun phrase, or a pronoun:

> Dick rode straight to the top of the building, *a brand-new hundred-floor skyscraper.*

The appositive describes *the building.*

> The band director, *Mr. Hickenlooper*, scheduled an extra rehearsal for the morning before the game.

The appositive identifies *The band director.*

> He ran out ahead of the pack, *a long and lean figure with nothing in his legs but bone and muscle.*

Ordinarily an appositive stands next to the word it describes. Here it is separated from that word—*He*—by six words, but since the appositive cannot refer to *pack*, the reader has no trouble connecting it to *He.*

> She begged all day for small change: *pennies, nickels, and dimes.*

The nouns in the appositive identify the *small change.*

2.9 Absolute Phrases

An **absolute phrase** is a modifier usually made from a noun or noun phrase and a participle. It modifies the whole of the base sentence to which it is attached:

> *Sails flapping,* the boat tugged at its mooring.

The participle may be expanded into a participle phrase:

> *Sails flapping in the brisk morning breeze,* the boat tugged at its mooring.

You can also make an absolute phrase with certain other combinations.

1. Noun and adverb:

> *Shoulders hunched,* Venturi zigzagged past the linebacker.

2. Noun and adverb phrase:

> Sloan sat back comfortably, *feet up on the desk.*

3. Noun and adjective:

> *Muscles taut,* he hefted the barbells to his chest.

4. Noun and adjective phrase:

> She waved to the crowd, *her face radiant with triumph.*

Finally, you can use various absolute phrases in succession:

> Venturi zigzagged past the linebacker, *shoulders hunched, arms hugging the ball, legs going like pistons.*
> *Hair golden, eyes blue, body slender and tanned,* he personified the California look.

Name _____ Date _____

Exercise 1. Recognizing Adjectives and Adverbs

Part A. In each of the following sentences, underline any adjectives and any nouns used in place of adjectives. Then draw an arrow from each word you have underlined to the word it modifies.

EXAMPLE

She sat on the dirty curbstone under the big arch of the
old gray bridge.

1. The quick brown fox jumps over the lazy dog.

2. In the bright light of the summer morning she ran over the
   wet grass.

3. The white surf rolled up over the dry sand like heavy cream.

4. Her speech was brilliant.

5. Birds filled the leafy trees.

6. A young man with a red beard took the empty seat.

7. The dingy walls look dark even on sunny days.

8. Fresh lemons are both nutritious and sour.

9. The weary hikers soaked their tender feet in the icy water of
   the brook.

10. The calm manner of the witness made a favorable impression on
    the jurors.

Part B. In each of the following sentences, underline any adverbs. Then draw an arrow from each word you have underlined to the word or word group it modifies.

EXAMPLE

The cat purred softly.

1. The car skidded dangerously.

2. Medical students usually work hard.

3. Joan is a daringly original painter.

4. Motorists have been advised to drive slowly.

5. Fortunately, I found my wallet.

6. The patients seldom complain.

7. The children loudly cheered the clowns.

8. The first violinist played brilliantly.

9. I felt gloriously free.

10. Newcomers always handle the explosives nervously.

Name _____ Date _____

Exercise 2.   Recognizing Adjective Phrases and Adverb Phrases

Part A.   In each of the following sentences, underline any adjective phrases. Then draw an arrow from each phrase you have underlined to the word it modifies.

EXAMPLE

A dinner without wine is like a day without sunshine.

1. The view from the top floor of the Prudential Building is spectacular.

2. My grandmother always serves me apple pie with vanilla ice cream.

3. Socks with holes are better than shoes without soles.

4. The sign on the rusty gate showed a hunter with a gun in his right hand.

5. The athletes on the squad are in excellent physical condition.

6. Amazingly enough, the golf ball in the cup was mine!

7. I sold the Harley-Davidson and bought a '75 Thunderbird in mint condition.

8. The customers at Brown's Department Store are always in a hurry.

9. The road to fame and fortune is seldom straight.

10. The clock on the mantelpiece in the living room ticked loudly.

Part B. In each of the following sentences, underline any adverb phrases. Then draw an arrow from each phrase you have underlined to the word it modifies.

EXAMPLE

Paul whooped, overjoyed at the news.

1. He left in a huff.

2. At noon we went to the airport.

3. After a long search I found my shoe under the sofa.

4. The car took the straightaway like a bullet.

5. The umpire was obviously hot under the collar.

6. Pleased with the verdict, the defense attorney smiled at her client.

7. During the storm the masts of five ships snapped like matchsticks.

8. A porpoise was caught in the net.

9. The heavy trunk fell to the floor with a thud.

10. The director is never impatient with subordinates.

Name _____ Date _____

Exercise 3. Using Adjectives and Adverbs

Part A. In each of the following sentences, choose from the pair of words in parentheses the one that is correct in the sentence, and write it in the blank at right.

EXAMPLE

George looked (handsome, handsomely) in a tuxedo.   *handsome*

1. Benwick reacted (calm, calmly) to the fire alarm.   _____

2. Freebright never talks (loud, loudly) in the classroom.   _____

3. Satin feels (smooth, smoothly).   _____

4. She won the first game (easy, easily).   _____

5. Jerome pitched (good, well) for five innings.   _____

6. The house looked (mysterious, mysteriously) in the moonlight.   _____

7. I was (real, really) amazed at the price.   _____

8. The chocolate dessert tasted (sweet, sweetly).   _____

9. Her voice sounded (strange, strangely) on the phone.   _____

10. She spoke (sensible, sensibly) during the meeting.   _____

Part B. In each of the following sentences, correct any errors in the use of an adjective or adverb. If a sentence is correct as it stands, write *Correct.*

EXAMPLE

Harry talks ~~loud~~ *loudly* on the phone.

1. The chef tasted his dessert carefully.

2. The old man spoke slow.

3. The doctor discovered a total new way of dieting.

4. Jerry always plays bad on a wet field.

5. Some of the audience grew sleepy after the intermission.

6. The coach shouted angry.

7. The corn has been growing steadily since last week's rainfall.

8. My watch has run good since it was cleaned.

9. The ambulance is usually quickly to arrive at the scene of an accident.

10. I have learned to drive cautious on icy roads.

Name_____ Date_____

Exercise 4.   Composing with Adjectives and Adverbs

Fill the blank in each of the following sentences with a suitable adjective, adjective phrase, adverb, or adverb phrase. Then in the blank at right indicate which one you have used.

EXAMPLES

The children laughed at the *funny* stories.

Adjective

Karen ran *out of the room*.

Adverb phrase

1. The _____ flag
   flapped in the breeze.   _____

2. He plunged into the _____
   water.   _____

3. Connie ripped the paper_____
   _____.   _____

4. The plants in the sun looked healthier
   than those_____.   _____

5. A _____ frog
   leaped out of the pond.   _____

6. _____, none of
   the passengers survived the crash.   _____

7. A woman with_____
   children cannot easily hold a full-time
   job.   _____

8. Professional musicians practice_____

   _____   _____

9. A friendly greeting is like a ray of sunshine after a week of _____
   days.   _____

10. One window_____
    was broken.   _____

11. The candidate gave a_____
    speech.   _____

12. A man_____was
    giving away free passes to the circus. _____

13. The_____ locomotive
    chugged steadily up the hill.   _____

14. _____a scream
    broke the stillness of the night. _____

15. I was amazed to get a letter_____

    _____.   _____

16. The baby slept_____

    _____.   _____

17. To the roar of the fans, he hit the ball

    _____.   _____

18. Acrophobia is fear_____

    _____.   _____

19. The suitcases were _____ . _____

20. Visitors to New York always want tick-
    ets_____ .   _____

Name _____ Date _____

Exercise 5. Forming Comparatives and Superlatives

Part A.   Fill the blank in each of the following sentences with the comparative form of the adjective or adverb given in parentheses. Express the idea of "more" or "less" as indicated.

EXAMPLE

Dolphins are **smarter** than sharks. (smart, *more*)

1. Bob is _____ than his father. (tall, *more*)

2. On the whole, adults learn foreign languages _____ than children do. (easily, *less*)

3. The old directions are _____ than the new ones. (confusing, *less*)

4. Cloudy days are sometimes _____ than sunny ones. (beautiful, *more*)

5. The team played _____ in the second half than it did in the first. (badly, *more*)

6. Joe's dog is _____ than his cat. (friendly, *more*)

7. I was _____ than he was. (eager, *less*)

8. The second set of photographs is _____ than the first set. (good, *more*)

9. Nights in the country are usually _____ than nights in the city. (quiet, *more*)

10. Sometimes muddy roads can be _____ than icy ones. (bad, *more*)

Part B. Fill the blank in each of the following sentences with the superlative form of the adjective or adverb given in parentheses. Express the idea of "most" or "least" as indicated.

EXAMPLE

This is the ___*most economical*___ car in the lot. (economical, *most*)

1. Of the five golfers in the contest, Sally hit the ball the _____ _____. (far, *most*)

2. I managed to get the _____ chair in the room. (comfortable, *least*)

3. Paul is the _____ member of his family. (bright, *most*)

4. That was the _____ mistake I ever made. (bad, *most*)

5. Of all the designs submitted, Benwick's is the _____ _____. (complex, *most*)

6. The _____ thing on the menu was coffee at $1.75 a cup. (expensive, *least*)

7. Which of the three roads is the _____? (old, *most*)

8. In the Kentucky Derby, my horse started the _____ _____ to the rail. (near, *most*)

9. Of his many supporters in the White House, which one served him the _____? (loyally, *most*)

10. Gary was the _____ actor in the show. (good, *most*)

Name_____ Date_____

Exercise 6. Recognizing and Writing Correct Comparisons

Part A. Each of the following consists of two sentences, one with a faulty comparison and the other with a comparison that is correct and complete. Circle the letter of the sentence in which the comparison is correct and complete.

EXAMPLE

(a) Girls mature sooner.
(b) Girls mature sooner than boys do.

1. (a) Bob is the faster runner on the college track team.
    (b) Bob is the fastest runner on the college track team.

2. (a) A horse is less intelligent than a dog.
    (b) A horse is least intelligent than a dog.

3. (a) Children learn foreign languages more easier than adults do.
    (b) Children learn foreign languages more easily than adults do.

4. (a) It was the most best birthday party I had ever had.
    (b) It was the best birthday party I had ever had.

5. (a) Susan gets answers quicker than anyone else.
    (b) Susan gets answers more quickly than anyone else.

6. (a) Uncle Pete is the oldest.
    (b) Uncle Pete is the oldest man in the town.

7. (a) Jesse Owens ran the most fastest race of his life.
    (b) Jesse Owens ran the fastest race of his life.

8. (a) A mule can drag a log more farther than a horse.
    (b) A mule can drag a log farther than a horse can.

9. (a) Of the two candidates Bert is the better qualified.
    (b) Of the two candidates Bert is the more better qualified.

10. (a) The bite of a horsefly is badder than the bite of a mosquito.
    (b) The bite of a horsefly is worse than the bite of a mosquito.

Part B. Revise any of the following sentences in which a comparison is incorrect or incomplete. If a sentence is correct as it stands, write *Correct.*

EXAMPLES

Tom is more smarter than his brother.

Tom is smarter than his brother.

Sally ran faster on the outdoor track.

Sally ran faster on the outdoor track than on the indoor one.

Hortense was the biggest cow.

Hortense was the biggest cow in the field.

1. During the Middle Ages the more powerful source of censorship in all of Europe was the Roman Catholic Church.

2. Blue whales are the largest.

3. The most highest speed yet attained by a jet-engined car is 613.995 miles per hour.

4. Her face is more rounder than mine.

5. For speed as well as economy, the best designed truck in the world cannot beat a railroad freight car.

6. The judge examined the evidence more careful than my lawyer ever did.

7. This model is the less expensive of the three.

8. Cold water is better for burns.

9. Of all the girls she studies the most hardest.

10. The world's more powerful tugboat is the *S. A. Wolraad Walte-made,* rated at 19,200 horsepower.

Name_____ Date_____

Exercise 7. Using Participles and Infinitives

Combine the sentences in each of the following pairs by using the italicized word or phrase in the second sentence as a modifier in the first.

EXAMPLE

She stuck her head out the window.
She was *grinning*.

Grinning, she stuck her head out the window.

1. The speaker nearly put me to sleep.
   He was *droning*.

2. In the bottom drawer I found a sheet of paper.
   The sheet of paper was *wrinkled*.

3. She steered the kayak expertly through the white water.
   The white water was *churning*.

4. Edison continued his work on the light bulb.
   He was *resisting the temptation to despair*.

5. The president vetoed the bill.
   His aim was *to curb congressional spending*.

6. The Chrysler Corporation borrowed several hundred million dollars from the federal government in 1980.
   Chrysler's purpose was *to avoid bankruptcy.*

7. The yawl sped through the waves.
   The boat was *driven by a stiff wind.*

8. The horse galloped off with a boy.
   The boy was *clinging desperately to its neck.*

9. Hank sat at the table.
   He was *eating fried eggs and mashed potatoes.*

10. He discovered a skeleton.
    He was *peering into the shadowy depths of a vault unused for years.*

11. Sam is going on a diet.
    He wants *to lose fifteen pounds by Christmas.*

12. The soldiers were eager.
    They wanted *to conquer the city.*

2.10   Placing Modifiers

In general, you should place a modifier close to its **headword**—the word or phrase it modifies. But different kinds of modifiers require somewhat different positions.

1. Adjectives normally precede their headword:

   a *large, red* ball

2. Adjective phrases usually follow their headword:

   the duffel bag *with white lettering.*

3. Adverbs can appear in various places near or next to their headword:

   He *always* handles the eggs *carefully.*

   Lately she has been working *hard.*

4. Adverb phrases belong near their headword:

   They jog *around the track before breakfast.*

   During the intermission the conductor refreshed himself *with a cold shower.*

5. Like adjectives, single participles normally precede their headword:

   the *smiling* girl

   a *broken* glass

6. Participle phrases can appear in various positions:

   The child treasures a scorecard *autographed by Ron Guidry.*

   Waving to newsmen, the president looked jubilant.

   The president, *scanning his notes,* prepared to speak.

   The boxer sank to his knees, *battered beyond caring and strength.*

7. Appositives ordinarily belong next to the noun or noun phrase they identify:

   All of us cheered the master of ceremonies, *a genial old-timer with a hundred jokes.*

8. Infinitives and infinitive phrases normally follow the noun or adjective they modify:

   Jake told us that Route 241 was definitely a road *to avoid.*

The cost of the new building was hard *to estimate.*

Determined *to reach* the summit by sunset, we set out at dawn.

mm When infinitives or infinitive phrases modify a whole clause, they can precede or follow the clause:

> *To gather all the hay before the rains came,* we had to work for ten hours straight.

> We had to work for ten hours straight *to gather all the hay before the rains came.*

9. Absolute phrases can precede or follow the clause they modify:

> *Its old timbers shifting,* the house creaked.
> The house creaked, *its old timbers shifting.*

You may not immediately know where to put a modifier when you are writing a long or complicated sentence. If so, simply add the modifier at the end; when you review the sentence, you can move the modifier if necessary to make its reference clear or to strengthen the impact of the sentence as a whole. As an example, consider the work of a writer who wanted to make one sentence out of four short ones she had written in her first draft:

> I spoke on the problem of chemical pollution.
> The pollution was in the Kanawha River.
> I gave my speech at the National 4-H Convention.
> I spoke as a delegate from Charleston, West Virginia.

To make one sentence from these four, she first combined them in the order in which she had written them:

> I spoke on the problem of chemical pollution in the Kanawha River at the National 4-H Convention as a delegate from Charleston, West Virginia.

Then she rearranged the modifiers so that the most important part of the sentence would appear in the most emphatic position, at the end:

> As a delegate from Charleston, West Virginia, I spoke at the National 4-H Convention on the problem of chemical pollution in the Kanawha River.

2.11 Misplaced Modifiers *mm*

A **misplaced modifier** is one that does not clearly point to its head-word—the word or phrase it modifies. Consider this example:

> *The final scene unites two characters who, in the beginning, had hated each other in a beautiful way.

In a beautiful way is supposed to modify *unites two characters,* but because of its position, it seems to modify *had hated each other.* The result is a confusing sentence. To clarify a sentence like this, put the modifier right next to its headword:

> The final scene unites in a beautiful way two characters who, in the beginning, had hated each other.

Now consider a sentence that appeared in a student's essay about American whalers:

> *Ships filled the harbor manned by fearless Yankees.

The sentence seems to say that the harbor was manned by fearless Yankees. Once again, the sentence becomes clear when the modifier is put right next to its headword:

> Ships manned by fearless Yankees filled the harbor.

2.12   Dangling Modifiers   *dg*

A **dangling modifier** is one that lacks a headword:

> *Parking the car, the right front fender was scraped.

Parking the car is a modifier, a participle phrase. After this modifier, the reader expects to find a headword telling who did the parking. But what turns up in the headword slot is *the right front fender,* and the rest of the sentence makes no reference to anyone who could have parked the car. To clarify the sentence, the writer must supply the correct headword for *parking the car* and put it directly after the modifier:

> Parking the car, *Janet* scraped the right front fender.

Consider a second example:

> *To walk again, an operation will be needed.

To walk again is a dangling modifier because the sentence fails to identify anyone who walks or might be able to walk. Once again, to clarify the sentence the writer must supply the correct headword, this time by identifying the person who wants to walk again:

> To walk again, *John* will need an operation.

Name _____ Date _____

Exercise 8. Adding and Arranging Modifiers

Combine the sentences in each of the following sets by treating the
first as the base sentence and using the italicized words from the other
sentences as modifiers. You may do some arranging of modifiers as
you add them, but after you have added all the modifiers, rearrange
them where necessary to stress the main point of the whole sentence
and to make its meaning clear. Delete any words you don't need.

EXAMPLE

I spoke on the problem of chemical pollution.
The pollution was *in the Kanawha River*.
I gave my speech *at the National 4-H Convention*.
I spoke *as a delegate from Charleston, West Virginia*.

COMBINED *I spoke on the problem of chemical pollution in the Kanawha River at the National 4-H Convention as a delegate from Charleston, West Virginia.*

REARRANGED: *As a delegate from Charleston, West Virginia, I spoke at the National 4-H Convention on the problem of chemical pollution in the Kanawha River.*

1. A young banker piled cash and securities into a wagon and took them to his home.
   It was *during the San Francisco earthquake.*
   The earthquake was *in 1906.*
   The banker was *named Amadeo Peter Giannini.*
   He went *with a guard of two soldiers.*
   His home was *in San Mateo.*

   COMBINED:

   REARRANGED:

2. He buried these assets.
   He did so *carefully.*
   He did so *in the middle of the night.*
   The assets were *valuable.*
   He buried them *in the garden.*
   The garden was *small.*
   It was *adjoining his house.*

   COMBINED:

   REARRANGED:

Name _____ Date _____

Exercise 8, *continued*

3. He set up a desk, put up a sign, and began doing business.
   This was *the next day.*
   The sign said *"Bank of Italy."*
   The desk was *open to all passersby.*
   It was *in the ruins of the city.*
   The ruins were *smoking.*

   COMBINED:

   REARRANGED:

4. Giannini's Bank of Italy eventually became the Bank of America.
   The Bank of America is a *commercial* bank.
   It is *the largest bank* of this kind *in the United States.*

   COMBINED:

   REARRANGED:

Name _____ Date _____

Exercise 9.   Recognizing Headwords and Modifiers

Part A.   In each of the following sentences a modifier is italicized. In the space below, identify its headword—the word or phrase that it modifies.

EXAMPLE

A man *in a bright red bow tie* greeted us at the door.

a man

1. *Moving into a new apartment,* Jean found a seven-foot-long boa constrictor in her dishwasher.

2. Parts of the Appian Way, *built in 312 B.C.,* are still being traveled.

3. *Unable to see anything,* I had to feel my way along.

4. The clothes *hanging on the line* flapped and danced in the brisk wind.

5. The horse stumbled over a beer can *left in the middle of the trail.*

6. The clock standing *on the mantelpiece* was an heirloom.

7. Because of their training, the cadets were quick *to carry out their orders.*

8. Elizabeth cherishes a table made *by her father.*

9. The photograph in the center *of the front page* shows the two winners of the raffle.

10. A local veterinarian has volunteered to talk to children *frightened of dogs.*

Part B. In each of the following sentences a headword is italicized. In the space below, identify any word or phrase that modifies it.

EXAMPLE

At the end of the poker game I went home with only *two* dollars.

only

1. Benedict Arnold's plot to surrender his command at West Point was only one of his dishonest, treacherous *acts.*

2. Before that he *had misused* his military authority.

3. He sought to betray *the trust* of his superiors.

4. After the war Arnold *was discharged* for dishonesty.

5. He finally became an unsuccessful *privateer.*

6. The thirsty hikers hesitated to drink the muddy *water* in the pond.

7. The fresh *coat* of red paint makes the barn look good.

8. Bob's comments about his pet raccoon were extremely *funny.*

9. The emergency crew *carried* an elderly woman from the burning building.

10. Arriving on schedule, *the Silver Arrow* brought three hundred tourists to the land of their dreams.

Name _____ Date _____

Exercise 10.   Recognizing Well-Placed Modifiers and Correcting Misplaced Modifiers

Part A.   Each of the following consists of two sentences, one with a misplaced modifier and the other with all modifiers well placed. Circle the letter of the sentence in which all modifiers are well placed.

EXAMPLE

    (a)   I shut the door to keep the dog from getting out at once.
    (b)   I shut the door at once to keep the dog from getting out.

1. (a)   Janice absentmindedly left her books in the theater after rehearsing for the play.
   (b)   Janice left her books in the theater after rehearsing for the play absentmindedly.

2. (a)   Matt abandoned his search for the missing tickets being late for class.
   (b)   Being late for class, Matt abandoned his search for the missing tickets.

3. (a)   The strong digestive acid in your stomach would burn a blister on the palm of your hand.
   (b)   In your stomach the strong digestive acid would burn a blister on the palm of your hand.

4. (a)   The scout troop tried to escape the cold wind and icy rain huddling in their tents.
   (b)   Huddling in their tents, the scout troop tried to escape the cold wind and icy rain.

5. (a)   The tornado left the town hall, the fire station, and a museum of irreplaceable local antiquities in ruins.
   (b)   The tornado left in ruins the town hall, the fire station, and a museum of irreplaceable local antiquities.

Part B. Revise any of the following sentences in which one or more modifiers are misplaced. If a sentence is correct as it stands, write *Correct.*

EXAMPLE

The scratching sounds worried us coming from inside the walls of the house.

The scratching sounds coming from inside the walls of the house worried us.

1. On the inside of the left arm sometimes pain indicates heart trouble.

2. Messages of pain reach the spinal cord at the same level from the arms and the heart.

3. Only a heart sends out such messages in danger.

4. The brain is confused by these unexpected messages from the endangered heart.

5. The brain refers the pain to solve its dilemma to a more familiar source, the arm.

Name _____ Date _____

Exercise 11.   Recognizing Well-Supported Modifiers and Correcting Dangling Modifiers

Part A.   Each of the following consists of two sentences, one with a dangling modifier and the other with all modifiers supported by headwords. Circle the letter of the sentence in which all modifiers are supported by headwords.

> EXAMPLE
>
> (a)   Parking the car, the right front fender was scraped.
> (b)   Parking the car, Janet scraped the right front fender.

1. (a)   The ice cracked while I was skating across the pond.
    (b)   The ice cracked while skating across the pond.

2. (a)   Hitting the brakes, the car skidded.
    (b)   As I hit the brakes, the car skidded.

3. (a)   Thirty dollars a week was earned by selling sandwiches at the football games.
    (b)   I earned thirty dollars a week by selling sandwiches at the football games.

4. (a)   Walking down Main Street on Sunday, there was no place open for lunch.
    (b)   Walking down Main Street on Sunday, we found no place open for lunch.

5. (a)   To cut taxes without increasing the national debt, government spending must also be cut.
    (b)   To cut taxes without increasing the national debt, the government must also cut its spending.

Part B. Revise any of the following sentences in which there is a dangling modifier. Either supply a headword as best you can, or reconstruct the whole sentence. If a sentence is correct as it stands, write *Correct*.

EXAMPLE

To walk again, an operation will be needed.

To walk again, John will need an operation.

1. To save money, the bus was taken instead of the plane.

2. Looking at the conclusion, several questions remain unanswered.

3. The house was left early in order to reach the store by eight o'clock.

4. Reading the book again, the main character seemed pompous and dull.

5. Speaking against the proposal, the governor called it irresponsible and unaffordable.

Name_____ Date _____

Exercise 12. Placing Modifiers Well and Supplying Headwords

Part A. Combine the sentences in each of the following pairs by using the italicized word or phrase in the second sentence as a modifier in the first. Be sure that each modifier clearly points to its headword.

EXAMPLE

On display at the museum was a collection of silverware.
The silverware was *made by Paul Revere.*

On display at the museum was a collection of silverware made by Paul Revere.

1. Environmental scientists monitor the coughing of fish.
   The scientists do this *to measure water pollution.*

2. St. Bernard dogs often find lost climbers in the Alps.
   The dogs are *gifted with an acute sense of hearing.*

3. Adam Smith was one of the first scholars to understand the central mechanisms of an unplanned economy.
   He is *the father of modern economics.*

4. The Greeks and Romans used steam-driven turbines as toys.
   This was the *only* way they used them.

5. The Incas united the huge area from southern Colombia to northern Chile and Argentina.
   They united it *under one government.*

Part B. Use each of the following phrases as a modifier in a sentence of your own. Be sure to supply a headword for each phrase.

EXAMPLE

before starting the car

Before starting the car, she checked the oil.

1. brutally silencing all opposition

2. reading the letter with a malicious gleam in his eye

3. to attend college at the present rate of tuition

4. casting for trout in the icy stream

5. to break the smoking habit

3

VERBAL NOUNS

A **verbal noun** is a present participle used as a noun or an infinitive used as a noun. It can also be a participle phrase or an infinitive phrase used as a noun. Verbal nouns enable you to treat an action as if it were a thing, and thus to get more action into your sentences:

> Mary's *singing* lifted my spirits.
> Spectators enjoy *the exploding of firecrackers.*
> *To win* was her only goal.
> The stunt man didn't want *to leap from the plane.*

3.1 Types of Verbal Nouns

Verbal nouns are of four types.

1. Present participle used as a noun:

> Some people dislike *exercising.*
> *Hiking* was her favorite pastime.

2. Infinitive used as a noun:

> The prisoner wanted *to sleep*, but could not.
> *To surrender* was unthinkable.

3. Participle phrase used as a noun:

> The workmen had no hope of *finishing the job before dark.*
> Vic's specialty is *kicking field goals.*
> *Teaching deaf children to talk* requires patience, skill, and faith.

4. Infinitive phrase used as a noun:

> One of the nation's goals is *to increase the production of steel.*
> The general's plan—*to launch a counterattack during the blizzard*—was a bold one.

(For the uses of the present participle as a modifier, see section 2.6, pp. 24-25; for the uses of the infinitive as a modifier, see section 2.7, pp. 25-26.)

3.2 Using Verbal Nouns

You can use verbal nouns to combine sentences in many ways. The most important are shown here:

1. Some playwrights direct their own plays.
   They like that.
   COMBINED: Some playwrights like *to direct their own plays.* [or] Some playwrights like *directing their own plays.*

2. She won the spelling bee.
   That delighted her.
   COMBINED: *To win the spelling bee* delighted her. [or] *Winning the spelling bee* delighted her. [or] It delighted her *to win the spelling bee.*

3. He led the parade.
   That was an honor for him.
   COMBINED: *To lead the parade* was an honor for him. [or] It was an honor for him *to lead the parade.* [or] *Leading the parade* was an honor for him.

4. Seymour broke the record.
   That made him a celebrity.
   COMBINED: *Seymour's breaking of the record* made him a celebrity.

You can turn a question into a verbal noun by using the infinitive after such words as *how, where, what, whom, whether,* and *when:*

Should she go or stay?
She did not know.
COMBINED: She did not know *whether to go or stay.*

3.3 Verbal Nouns and Ordinary Nouns

Sometimes you can turn a sentence into a noun phrase by turning the verb into an ordinary noun instead of a verbal noun. See how these sentences can be combined:

Ryan criticized the plan.
That surprised everyone.
COMBINED: *Ryan's criticizing of the plan* surprised everyone. [or] *Ryan's criticism of the plan* surprised everyone.

The verb *criticized* can become the verbal noun *criticizing* or the ordinary noun *criticism.*

3.4   Misusing Verbal Nouns   *mvn*

Normally a noun or pronoun used before a verbal noun ending in *-ing* should be in the possessive case:

>*Bob chattering got on our nerves.
>REVISED: *Bob's chattering* got on our nerves.

>*Everyone enjoyed him singing.
>REVISED: Everyone enjoyed his singing.

(For a full discussion of case in pronouns, see section 9.5, pp. 145–48.)
   Normally a verbal noun that follows a possessive noun or a possessive pronoun (such as *his, her,* or *my*) should not be directly followed by a noun or noun phrase:

>*His calling the meeting took everyone by surprise.

Add *of* after *calling:*

>His calling of the meeting took everyone by surprise.

But you can skip the *of* when the verbal noun follows a preposition:

>The static interfered with our hearing the news.

3. Verbal Nouns

Name _____ Date _____

Exercise 1.   Recognizing Verbal Nouns

In each of the following sentences, underline the verbal noun or nouns.

EXAMPLES

On weekends many students enjoy <u>sleeping</u>.
One of my hobbies is <u>collecting old arrowheads</u>.

1. Ordering the army to cross the Bronze River was a mistake.

2. Melissa loved to play with the cat.

3. Barbara was unaccustomed to speaking before large groups of people.

4. To err is human.

5. At this moment my only concern is to pass the physics examination.

6. A common mistake of many vacationers is entering the big woods without a compass.

7. Because of labor costs, the manager may decide to close the store at noon on Saturdays.

8. The detective's most recent success—solving the Riddley case—has earned him a promotion.

9. To rely on yourself is to learn your own strengths and weaknesses.

10. Veterans of the rush hour avoid taking Kentucky Avenue between 4 and 5 P.M.

Name _____ Date _____

Exercise 2.   Correcting Misused Verbal Nouns

Revise any of the following sentences in which a verbal noun is misused. If a sentence is correct as it stands, write *Correct*.

EXAMPLE

Bob chattering got on our nerves.

Bob's chattering got on our nerves.

1. No one in the building appreciated him yodeling at 5:00 A.M.

2. The tenor hitting a high C thrilled the audience.

3. The new owners plan to demolish the barn completely.

4. The lion roaring frightened the children.

5. The colonel ordering a general inspection at 4:00 A.M. left everyone groggy.

6. To report the facts accurately is the duty of a good reporter.

7. The police objected to us playing basketball in the park.

8. The professor was amazed at me finding a solution to the problem.

9. Voters were impressed by one of his promises—to review thoroughly the country's trade agreements with Japan.

10. Calhoun handling the investigation was sharply criticized.

3. Verbal Nouns

Name_____ Date_____

Exercise 3.   Sentence Combining with Verbal Nouns

Combine the sentences in each of the following pairs by turning one sentence into a verbal noun and joining it to the other.

EXAMPLE

Sarah washed the dog.
She hated that.

Sarah hated washing the dog.

1. Sandy shouted.
   That woke me up.

2. She waited for hours.
   That made her anxious.

3. Harrington negotiated a compromise.
   That action kept the workers on the job.

4. She built the house without any help.
   That took her a long time.

5. Where could he find a job?
   He didn't know.

6. Some sculptors work with wood.
   They specialize in that.

7. Sheila collects seashells.
   That is Sheila's hobby.

8. He ran twenty miles in two hours.
   That left him exhausted.

9. She lost the match.
   That depressed her.

10. Vivian organized the conference.
    Everyone admired that.

4

COORDINATION

4.1 Using Coordination

To **coordinate** two or more parts of a sentence is to give them the same rank and role by making them grammatically similar:

> Thermal clothing should keep you *warm, dry,* and *comfortable.* [three adjectives]
> Store the vegetables *under the eaves* or *in the cellar.* [two adverb phrases]
> *The coin was definitely old,* but *it was not worth much.* [two clauses]

4.2 Compound Phrases

You can coordinate single words or phrases in a **compound phrase** to show one of the following relations:

1. Addition

> They were tired and hungry.

2. Contrast

> He was gruff but likable.

3. Choice

> On Friday nights she watched TV or went to the disco.

Joining the Parts of a Compound Phrase

The parts of a compound phrase should normally be joined by one of the means listed here.

1. One or more conjunctions, such as *and, yet, or, but,* or *nor:*

> They were clever *and* funny.
> The house was old *but* sturdy.

69

2. A comma:

> He liked nothing better than a fat, juicy hamburger.

3. A comma plus a conjunction:

> The house was big, old, *and* drafty.

When a compound phrase has three or more items, you normally need a comma plus a conjunction between the last two. Many writers also use a comma before *but* when it joins two phrases. Compare:

> ·He was gruff *but* likable.
> She won the argument, *but* lost a friend.

4. A pair of correlatives, such as *not only . . . but also, both . . . and, either . . . or,* or *neither . . . nor:*

> They were *not only* hungry *but also* homeless.
> Edison worked *both* night *and* day on his inventions.

4.3 Using Compound Sentences

A compound sentence joins two or more simple sentences to show one of the following relations between them:

1. Addition

> The battle was fierce, and many were killed.

2. Contrast

> The engine sounded good, but the body had been eaten up by rust.

3. Cause and effect

> Auto makers normally use huge quantities of steel; trouble in the auto industry, therefore, means trouble for the steel industry too.

4. Choice

> On Thanksgiving Day we all drove to my grandmother's house, or she came to visit us.

4.4 Making Compound Sentences

A compound sentence consists of two or more independent clauses. An **independent clause** is a group of words that contains a subject and a predicate and that could stand by itself as a simple sentence. Two or more simple sentences make a compound sentence:

> SIMPLE SENTENCES
>
> S   P
> They / fought bravely.

```
    S          P
They / were overwhelmed.
```

COMPOUND SENTENCE

INDEPENDENT CLAUSE   INDEPENDENT CLAUSE
[S] They / [P] fought bravely,   but [S] they / [P] were overwhelmed.

The compound sentence preserves the whole of each simple sentence in an independent clause.

4.5   Joining Independent Clauses

The independent clauses of a compound sentence should normally be joined in one of three ways: with a semicolon, with a conjunction, or with a conjunctive adverb.

The Semicolon

A semicolon alone can join two independent clauses when the relation between them is obvious:

> Some customers like the new check-out system; others find it a nuisance.

Conjunctions

A **conjunction** can show a relation between words, phrases, or clauses. Conjunctions used between clauses include *for* and *so* as well as those listed earlier—*and, yet, or, but,* and *nor.* A conjunction used between clauses is usually preceded by a comma:

> We are all worms, *but* I am a glowworm.   —Winston Churchill

Conjunctive Adverbs

A **conjunctive adverb** is a word or phrase that indicates the relation between the clauses it joins, as a conjunction does. But a conjunctive adverb is usually weightier and more formal than a conjunction:

> The Russians stopped short of invading Poland after the outbreak of strikes there; *nevertheless,* the threat of an invasion made the workers cautious.

Conjunctive adverbs include such words and phrases as *however, still, then, thus, therefore, consequently, similarly, nevertheless, in addition, for example, in contrast,* and *on the other hand.*

    A conjunctive adverb used between the clauses of a compound sentence is preceded by a semicolon and in most cases followed by a comma:

> The river sustains many forms of wildlife; *in addition,* it gives the neighborhood children a good place to swim.

No comma is needed after *then* or *thus:*

> The ice boomed, cracked, and split; then we sank into the bone-chilling water.

Though a conjunction always stands between the two clauses it joins, a conjunctive adverb can be placed within the second clause:

> The old bridge could no longer support heavy traffic; at the town meeting, therefore, the selectmen asked voters to approve the building of a new one.

In this sentence the second clause is preceded by a semicolon, and the conjunctive adverb is set off by commas. But when the conjunctive adverb is placed within the base predicate of the second clause, it need not be set off by commas:

> The old bridge can no longer support heavy traffic; the selectmen have *therefore* asked voters to approve the building of a new one.

Here *therefore* appears between the two parts of the verb in the second clause—*have* and *asked.*

Summary

The independent clauses (IC) of a compound sentence must normally be joined in one of the following three ways:

1. ___IC___ ; ___IC___ .
2. ___IC___ , conjunction ___IC___ .
3. ___IC___ ; conjunctive adverb ___IC___ .
   (placement optional)

Overusing *and*

Use *and* sparingly in compound sentences. A series of clauses strung together by *and* soon becomes boring:

> We went to the museum, and we saw the skeleton of a dinosaur, and we ate lunch, and we took a walk in the park.

To break the monotony of compounding with *and,* substitute other linking words, or other constructions:

> At the museum we saw the skeleton of a dinosaur; then we ate lunch and took a walk in the park.

(For more on alternatives to compounding with *and,* see the discussion of subordination, chapter 6, pp. 99–117.)

Name_____ Date _____

Exercise 1.　Recognizing Compound Phrases

Part A.　Each of the following sentences includes a compound phrase that is formed by the coordination of two or more single words. Underline this phrase.

EXAMPLE

The parking lot has spaces for <u>cars, trucks, and buses</u>.

1. During the play the audience laughed, wept, shuddered, and cheered.

2. Either Bob or Harry will drive the bus to Middletown.

3. Passengers have a choice of beverages: tea, coffee, milk, or cola.

4. The beams under the porch are old but strong.

5. The attendants are trained to speak both clearly and politely.

6. Walls, roofs, and towers crumbled in the earthquake.

7. Weary, hot, and thirsty, the brave company nevertheless struggled on.

8. Boys and girls ran gaily down the corridor.

9. The ballerina leaped, pirouetted, and bowed.

10. The men were sullen and suspicious.

Part B.   Each of the following sentences includes a compound phrase that is formed by the coordination of two or more phrases. Underline this phrase.

EXAMPLE

The miser hid coins <u>in flowerpots, behind window frames, and under the carpet.</u>

1. The prisoners are deprived of exercise and forbidden to talk during meals.

2. Lacking modern weapons but having old-fashioned courage, the guerrillas have waged a successful campaign for over two years.

3. Candidates apply for a position in the news department or with the television crew.

4. The firemen wanted not to break the window but to open it.

5. The exercise consists of three movements: raising both arms over your head, twisting your upper body to the left, and turning your head to the right.

6. The brave soldier lost his life but saved his honor.

7. Bud turned on the light and settled down to read.

8. The flashlight played over the cobweb-covered beams, down the walls, and along the dusty floor.

9. We traveled over the river and through the woods.

10. Standing by the door and smoking a cigarette, he seemed nervous.

Name _____ Date _____

Exercise 2.   Making Compound Phrases

Combine the sentences in each of the following sets by using a compound phrase. Add commas and suitable conjunctions where necessary.

EXAMPLE

Harry must follow the doctor's orders.
Otherwise Harry must remain an invalid.

Harry must follow the doctor's orders or remain an invalid.

1. Seniors may attend the president's reception.
   Seniors may talk with the guest of honor.
   Seniors may help to greet other dignitaries.

2. In the ancient pentathlon the athlete threw the discus.
   In the ancient pentathlon the athlete hurled the javelin.
   In the ancient pentathlon the athlete ran a footrace.
   In the ancient pentathlon the athlete wrestled.
   In the ancient pentathlon the athlete did a broad jump.

3. Are we too gullible?
   Are we too suspicious?

4. In the Israeli war of independence women fought bravely.
   In the Israeli war of independence women fought fiercely.

5. Students were dressed in bright puffy vests.
   Students were dressed in ragged army jackets.
   Students were dressed in college sweatshirts.

6. Economists often classify economic resources into three categories.
   One category is land.
   One category is labor.
   One category is capital.

7. Nate wanted to play on the basketball team.
   He wanted to work on the school newspaper.
   He wanted to sing in the chorus.

8. The purpose of the bill now before Congress is to develop land.
   The purpose is also to provide jobs for youths in rural areas.

9. The old woman picked through the rubble.
   She gathered up a few pictures.

10. The prisoners would not eat.
    They would not work.

4. Coordination

Name_____ Date_____

Exercise 3.   Making Compound Sentences with Conjunctions

Combine the sentences in each of the following sets by using a comma and a suitable conjunction—*and, yet, or, but, nor, for,* or *so.* Write down just enough to show how you are combining the sentences.

EXAMPLE

The Boy Scouts were proud of their float.
They had worked overtime to complete it before the parade.

float, for they

1. Everyone wanted an invitation.
   Only a few students got one.

2. Roberto must learn his lines by tomorrow.
   He will be fired.

3. Mike wants to get a degree in chemistry.
   He does not want to spend his afternoons in the lab.

4. Universities pay special attention to undergraduates now.
   Their graduate-student enrollment is down.

5. Caroline is determined to learn hang gliding.
   With luck she will succeed.

6. Simon worked all night to develop the prints.
   No one appreciated his effort.

7. The soprano fainted in the middle of the first act.
   The rest of the performance had to be canceled.

8. My summer job paid well.
   By October I had spent my summer earnings.

9. They had no insurance on the fire-gutted house.
   They could not easily afford to rebuild it.

10. An icy wind blew through the chinks in the old log cabin.
    We wrapped ourselves in blankets to keep warm.

Name_____ Date_____

Exercise 4. Making Compound Sentences with Conjunctive Adverbs

Combine the sentences in each of the following sets by using a semi-colon and a suitable conjunctive adverb, such as *therefore, as a result, nevertheless,* or *consequently.* Write down just enough to show how you are combining the sentences.

EXAMPLE

Two of the trainees have neither the intelligence nor the diligence to learn the required lessons.
They will be dismissed from the program.

lessons; consequently, they

1. Chemical wastes in the environment can seriously endanger people's health.
    The chemicals dumped in Love Canal caused sickness, genetic damage, and even death.

2. In 1955 a black woman passenger was arrested in Montgomery, Alabama, for refusing to move to the back of the bus.
    The blacks of Montgomery began a boycott of the city bus lines.

3. The Chinese originated papermaking.
    The Muslims developed the process and passed it on to the West.

4. In the 1936 Olympics a black American named Jesse Owens won the 100-meter race.
    Another black American, Ralph Metcalfe, came in second.

5. After Russia's invasion of Afghanistan the United States refused to participate in the Moscow Olympics of 1980.
    Many of our allies did participate.

6. In the nineteenth century valves were added to trumpets and horns.
   Wagner and Tchaikovsky could write melodies for the horn that would have been unplayable in the time of Haydn and Mozart.

7. Many people found the new symphony baffling, unmelodious, and tedious.
   Its quiet intensity and subtlety made a profound impression on sophisticated music lovers.

8. Dana lost her handbag during the demonstration.
   She had no money and no means of identification.

9. With sails furled, the grand old three-masted ship entered the harbor.
   It gradually approached the pier.

10. The president sought to cut government spending for social programs.
    He wanted to raise spending on defense.

4.6 Comma Splices *cs*

The **comma splice**, also called the "comma fault," is the error of join-ing two independent clauses with nothing but a comma:

> *The household was teeming with activity, in the kitchen an army of cooks was baking tarts, decorating sugar cookies, and preparing apple pies.

The meaning calls for a full stop between *activity* and *in,* but the comma doesn't provide one. To correct the error, you can do one of three things.

1. Put a conjunction after the comma:

> The household was teeming with activity, and in the kitchen an army of cooks was baking tarts, decorating sugar cookies, and preparing apple pies.

2. Replace the comma with a semicolon:

> The household was teeming with activity; in the kitchen an army of cooks was baking tarts, decorating sugar cookies, and preparing apple pies.

3. Replace the comma with a period, making two sentences.

> The household was teeming with activity. In the kitchen an army of cooks was baking tarts, decorating sugar cookies, and preparing apple pies.

Sometimes a comma splice occurs when the second clause in a sentence begins with a conjunctive adverb:

> *Inspectors detected a fissure in the engine block, as a result, they called a halt to production.

As a result is a conjunctive adverb, and a conjunctive adverb used be-tween two clauses must be preceded by a semicolon:

> Inspectors detected a fissure in the engine block; as a result, they called a halt to production.

Alternatively, you can use a period, making two sentences:

> Inspectors detected a fissure in the engine block. As a result, they called a halt to production.

4.7 Fused Sentences *fus*

A **fused sentence** runs two independent clauses together with no punc-tuation or conjunction between them:

> *Toddlers are welcome nurses are always on hand to supervise the ac-tivities.

Here the first independent clause simply pushes into the second, and the reader scarcely knows where one clause ends and the other begins. To correct the error, you can do one of three things.

1. Use a comma and a conjunction between the two clauses:

> Toddlers are welcome, and nurses are always on hand to supervise the activities.

2. Put a semicolon at the end of the first clause:

> Toddlers are welcome; nurses are always on hand to supervise the activities.

3. Put a period at the end of the first clause. You will then have two sentences:

> Toddlers are welcome. Nurses are always on hand to supervise the activities.

4. Coordination

Name_____ Date _____

Exercise 5.   Recognizing and Correcting Comma Splices and Fused
               Sentences, I

Each of the following may be a fused sentence or include a comma
splice. Where you find one of these errors, identify it by writing *fus*
(for fused sentence) or *cs* (for comma splice) in the blank at right.
Then correct the error by rewriting the faulty part of the sentence,
using a semicolon or a comma plus a suitable conjunction. If a sentence is correct as it stands, write *Correct*.

EXAMPLES

The life preserver was slowing me down I abandoned
it.

down, so I

fus

Commercial fishermen are angry, they oppose the use
of oil rigs close to the fishing grounds.

angry; they

cs

1. Among men the prime physical age is about twenty
   the prime mental age is about fifty.   _____

2. "In God we trust" was not the motto on the first
   coin minted in the United States, the first motto was
   "Mind your own business."   _____

3. Unmanned space probes eliminate the risk of death,
   furthermore, they cost much less than manned space
   flights.   _____

4. The two pits on the side of the rattlesnake's head
   enable him to detect the presence of a warm-blooded
   animal even in the dark, for the pits are sensitive to
   the slightest change in temperature.   _____

5. Recent college graduates sometimes find that their new jobs barely pay for food and a shabby apartment living at home, therefore, saves them years of scrimping.

6. Sigmund Freud was the world's authority on sex in his day, he ended his own sexual activity at about age forty.

7. Polly doesn't need the new umbrella she has found her old one.

8. Sequoya had little knowledge of English contact with the white men, however, showed him the importance of reading and writing.

9. I fumbled for words; my phrases came in staccato bursts.

10. The sea turned warm yellow sunlight played on the waves.

Name_____ Date _____

Exercise 6. Recognizing and Correcting Comma Splices and Fused Sentences, II

This exercise continues the work of the preceding exercise. Each of the following may be a fused sentence or include a comma splice. Where you find one of these errors, identify it by writing *fus* (for fused sentence) or *cs* (for comma splice) in the blank at right. Then correct the error by rewriting the faulty part of the sentence, using a semicolon or a comma plus a suitable conjunction. If a sentence is correct as it stands, write *Correct*.

EXAMPLES

The radiator kept banging all night I couldn't sleep a wink.   *fus*

night, so I

Our new wood stove is highly efficient, we get eight hours of heat from only three logs.   *cs*

efficient; we get

1. Terry liked sky diving, but she liked motorcycle racing more.   _____

2. The railroad ran along the river by our house, we could find our way home by following the tracks.   _____

3. Toby climbed the red maple tree Sam found him anyway.   _____

4. It was May snow still lay under the branches of the thick pines.   _____

5. In 1948 defectors wrote about life under Stalin, thus the West learned of his ruthless purges.   _____

6. Support the two-party system one party a week is not enough. _____

7. Alex escaped from prison; then he left the country. _____

8. There she sat she had not moved for hours. _____

9. The French revolutionaries executed King Louis XVI and Queen Marie Antoinette in 1793, likewise, the Russian revolutionaries executed Czar Nicholas II and the Empress Alexandra in 1918. _____

10. On the one hand, Iran held the hostages for over a year on the other hand, it released them in accordance with a painstakingly negotiated agreement. _____

Name _____ Date _____

Exercise 7.   Review: Correcting Comma Splices and Fused Sentences in a Passage

In each of the following passages, correct any fused sentences and comma splices by rewriting the faulty segments, as shown in the example.

EXAMPLE

1   Since World War II, Sweden has clung to a policy of neutral-
2   ity it has often served as a mediator between quarreling na-
3   tions. Swedish troops are mobilized not to fight but to quell
4   fighting, in fact, they have served as peace-keeping forces in
5   Israel, the Congo, and Cyprus. Yet two Swedish statesmen
6   have been killed while seeking peace. Count Folke Bernadotte
7   was assassinated during a peace mission to Israel, likewise,
8   Dag Hammarskjöld died in a plane crash in Africa.

lines 1-2: neutrality. It
line 4: fighting; in fact,
line 7: Israel; likewise,

1   A. The clarinet has a single reed, a small piece of cane attached to its
2   mouthpiece the instrument produces a clear, flowing tone, sharp
3   and strong on the high notes, relaxed in the middle range, reso-
4   nant and cool in the low register, its range in pitch and volume
5   is remarkably wide, as a result, it is particularly well-suited to
6   playing melody.

1 B. Ski jumping is done on a hill that is especially designed for that
2   purpose, a jumping hill is made up of four parts: the inrun, the
3   takeoff, the landing, and the outrun. The inrun is the steep slope
4   on which the jumper picks up his speed at the end of the inrun
5   is the takeoff, where he becomes airborne, and next comes the
6   landing, a part of the hill on which the jumper lands the land-
7   ing continues into the outrun, which allows room to slow down
8   and stop.   /

5

PARALLEL CONSTRUCTION

5.1 Why Choose Parallelism?

A **parallel construction** consists of two or more elements that are grammatically alike. By using parallel construction, also called "parallelism," you enhance the coordination of words, phrases, and clauses in a sentence, and you thereby highlight their meaning. Your expression becomes both clear and elegant:

> Arrogance is at once *the mask* and *the mark* of insecurity.
> Governments that make *peaceful change impossible* will make *violent change inevitable.*   —John F. Kennedy

5.2 Using Parallelism

Kinds of Parallelism

When you have two or more items in a list, a series, a contrast, a choice, a statement of equivalence, or a comparison, put all of the items in the same grammatical form.

1. List

> Unlike many other movie heroes, King Kong was *tall, dark,* and *ugly.* [three adjectives]

2. Series

> They fought *in the streets, in the alleyways, on the rooftops,* and *in the courtyards.* [four prepositional phrases]

3. Contrast

> *Slowly* but *steadily* they advanced. [two adverbs]

4. Choice

> Tourists can reach the summit *by taking the funicular railway* or *by climbing the steps on the eastern slope.* [two participle phrases]

5. Statement of equivalence

> *Hawks* are *predators*. [two nouns]

6. Comparison

> *Skiing on ice* is harder than *skating on it*. [two participle phrases]

Parallelism with Correlatives

When using a pair of correlatives, be sure that the word or word group following the first member of the pair is parallel with the word or word group following the second. The principal correlatives are *both . . . and, not only . . . but also, either . . . or, neither . . . nor,* and *whether . . . or.*

> Michelangelo was both *a sculptor* and *a painter*. [two noun phrases]
> We found mice not only *in the cupboard* but also *under the sink*. [two prepositional phrases]

5.3 Faulty Parallelism //

When two or more parts of a sentence are parallel in meaning, you should coordinate them fully by making them parallel in form. If you don't, your sentence will be marred by **faulty parallelism.** Here are some examples of this error and of ways to correct it.

1. *The mayor has said that all patrolmen should march in the parade and to attend the rally.

Here items parallel in meaning are not parallel in grammatical form. The terms describing the two actions required of the patrolmen do not line up; *march* is the bare form of the verb, and *to attend* is an infinitive. You can fix the sentence by using the bare form for both:

> The mayor has said that all patrolmen should *march* in the parade and *attend* the rally.

2. Some old-timers claim that a dry August means a wet October and warm days in January signal blizzards in March.

To highlight the parallelism here, use *that* before each of the parallel elements:

> Some old-timers claim *that a dry August means a wet October* and *that warm days in January signal blizzards in March.*

3. *The farmers will either find ways to cut their costs, or the banks will lower the interest rate on loans.

Since correlatives mark parallelism, they should be followed by grammatically parallel elements, in this instance complete clauses:

> Either *the farmers will find ways to cut their costs,* or *the banks will lower the interest rate on loans.*

Name _____ Date _____

Exercise 1. Recognizing Parallel Elements

In each of the following sentences, underline the parallel elements and circle the conjunction or pair of correlatives used to join them.

EXAMPLE

In December the days are often sunny (but) cold.

1. Commuters have been asked to use public transportation or to join a car pool.

2. He had not only bribed officials but also stolen secret documents.

3. Under Mao millions of Chinese died not of sickness but of bullets, of torture, and of starvation.   —George Beckmann

4. Hemingway's style is crisp, laconic, and understated.

5. The two main advantages of the helicopter are its ability to hover and its ability to land in restricted space.

6. Recently, scientists have begun to think that evolution is not always gradual, but sometimes sudden.

7. In lasers, either glass or gases serve to amplify light.

8. Playing football and holding a job kept Jeff busy.

9. The politician sought to gain reelection as well as to salvage his reputation.

10. A preadolescent may rebel at going to bed, keeping his room clean, or wearing suitable clothes.

11. Jackals encourage their young to stay in their home territory by sharing food with them, grooming them, and playing with them.

12. Controlling pollution in the air and in the water is a major objective of the Sierra Club.

13. Panting with fatigue but glowing with victory, Caroline dashed across the finish line first.

14. Buying new clothes, having her hair done, and making up her face occupied most of her waking hours.

15. Staring fearlessly at the coming truck, he neither blinked nor flinched.

16. The effectiveness of your writing depends not only on the number of words you know but also on the precision with which you use them.

17. After lunch he read the newspaper and took a nap.

18. He could either drop the course or risk failing it.

19. Fish farmers have found a new way to improve the oyster's chances of survival and to shorten its maturing time.

20. The various shapes of the cells in the human body include tubes, spheres, and cubes.

Name _____ Date _____

Exercise 2.   Composing with Parallelism

Each of the following includes a set of parallel elements and, in parentheses, a connecting word or a pair of correlatives. Write a sentence in which you use the term given in parentheses to join the parallel elements.

EXAMPLE

in my bureau / on the desk (either . . . or)

I had left my wallet either in my bureau or on the desk.

1. old / frisky (but)

2. to register for a term in Munich / to continue working in the physics laboratory (whether . . . or)

3. difficult to understand / boring to think about (not only . . . but also)

4. sized up the professor / made his pitch (and)

5. cold / rejecting / hostile (and)

6. to accept the role of wife and mother / to make a career for herself (or)

7. nights / weekends (both . . . and)

8. fear of failure / fear of success (not only . . . but also)

9. a meal / a bed for the night (neither . . . nor)

10. to remain an amateur / to turn professional (whether . . . or)

Name_____ Date_____

Exercise 3.   Correcting Faulty Parallelism

In each of the following, correct any faulty parallelism by rewriting the incorrect part of the sentence. If a sentence is correct as it stands, write *Correct*.

EXAMPLE

My grandfather said that I could live at the farm during his absence and to notify the police when I got there.

and that I should notify the police when I got there.

1. At various times Allison pictured herself exploring the Amazon jungle, climbing Mount Everest, and as someone who acted on Broadway.

2. Astronauts must be intelligent, cool-headed, and have exceptional health.

3. Pacing up and down, scowling at the referee, and cursing under his breath, the coach felt utterly frustrated.

4. In the Middle Ages most people believed that the earth was stationary and the universe to revolve around it.

5. More frequently now, men are discarding old *macho* attitudes and women insist on their right to freedom of opportunity.

6. A patient with mercury poisoning is apt to tremble uncontrollably and then he or she gets disoriented.

7. Roger stared at the audience with his mouth dry and his mind was blank.

8. The colonel told his officers to get their men up at 3:30 and that the officers should start the war games at dawn.

9. The committee rejected the amendment, shelved the proposal, and all questions were ignored.

10. In our society the aged lack status and they are not powerful.

5. Parallel Construction

Name_____ Date_____

Exercise 4.   Sentence Combining with Parallelism

Combine the sentences in each of the following sets into one or at most two sentences, using parallelism wherever appropriate.

EXAMPLE

The old men in the nursing home are encouraged to exercise daily.
They are encouraged to eat in the dining room.
They are encouraged to attend the evening social activity.
The old women are encouraged to do the same things too.
As a result, they are often livelier than patients in other nursing homes.
Their health is better too.

Both the old men and the old women in the nursing home are encouraged to exercise daily, eat in the dining room, and attend the evening social activity; as a result, they are often livelier and healthier than patients in other nursing homes.

1. In different states condemned prisoners have been electrocuted.
   They have been hanged.
   They have been gassed.
   In Utah they can choose to be hanged.
   In Utah they can choose to be shot.

2. The phrase "James brothers" means one thing in the history of the wild West.
It has a different meaning in the history of American culture.
Frank James was a notorious outlaw.
Jesse James was a notorious outlaw.
William James was a celebrated writer.
Henry James was a celebrated writer.

3. Unmanned spacecraft vary in diameter.
Their diameter ranges from a few inches to several hundred feet.
They also vary in shape.
Their shape ranges from boxlike to cigar-like.

4. Contrary to popular opinion, the behavior of women is no more capricious than the behavior of men.
Women don't behave more mysteriously than men do.
Women don't behave more emotionally than men do.

5. Amsterdam is known for the beauty of its canals.
Its narrow gabled houses are beautiful too.
And so are its tree-lined streets.

6

SUBORDINATION

6.1 Using Subordination

Subordination enables you to show the relative importance of the parts of a sentence. To use **subordination** is to make one or more parts of a sentence depend on the part that is most important to you.

You can subordinate a word or phrase in a sentence by using it as a modifier. (For a full discussion of modifiers, see chapter 2, pp. 19–58.) Likewise, you can subordinate an entire clause in a sentence by using it as a subordinate clause.

6.2 Subordinate Clauses

A **subordinate clause** (also called a "dependent clause") is a group of words that has its own subject and predicate but cannot stand alone as a sentence. It must be connected to or included in a **main clause**— a clause that can stand by itself as a sentence:

MAIN CLAUSE	SUBORDINATE CLAUSE
Priscilla was hit by a brick	which fell from the roof.

SUBORDINATE CLAUSE	MAIN CLAUSE
When the president is seated,	the concert will begin.

MAIN CLAUSE

SUBORDINATE CLAUSE

[S] What I want /   [P] is a motorcycle.

A subordinate clause can be a noun clause, an adjective clause, or an adverb clause. Each of these will be discussed in turn.

6.3 Noun Clauses

A **noun clause** is a clause used as a noun within a sentence. Compare these sentences:

1. *Something* left me worried.
2. *The speech* left me worried.
3. *What the speaker said about inflation* left me worried.

In sentence 1, the subject is a noun; in sentence 2, it is a noun phrase; in sentence 3, it is a noun clause—a clause used as a noun. A noun clause begins with a word like *whoever, whichever, whatever, who, that, what, how, why, when,* or *where.* It can be used as a subject, an object, a predicate noun, or an appositive.

1. Noun clause as subject:

Where the ship sank is unknown.

2. Noun clause as object of a verb:

They ate *whatever they could find.*

3. Noun clause as object of a preposition:

A prize will go to *whoever finishes the race.*

4. Noun clause as predicate noun:

Her suggestion is *that the deans meet with small groups of freshmen.*

6.4 Adjective (Relative) Clauses

An **adjective clause,** sometimes called a "relative clause," normally begins with a relative pronoun (*which, that, who, whom,* or *whose*) and normally modifies the word or phrase that comes before it. An adjective clause can be used to combine two sentences that refer to the same person or thing:

Newspapers want reporters of a certain kind.
Reporters of this kind can meet deadlines regularly.

COMBINED: Newspapers want reporters *who can meet deadlines regularly.*

A company of a certain kind is likely to provoke a strike.
This kind of company ignores the problems of its workers.

COMBINED: A company *that ignores the problems of its workers* is likely to provoke a strike.

Relative Pronouns and Antecedents

A **relative pronoun** normally introduces an adjective clause. The **antecedent** of the relative pronoun, which normally comes before it, is the word, phrase, or clause to which it refers. Relative pronouns referring to persons are *who* (subject case), *whom* (object case), *whose* (possessive case), and *that*. (For more on case, see section 9.5, pp. 145–48.) Relative pronouns referring to things are *which* and *that*. In addition, *when* and *where* are sometimes used as relative pronouns. Here are some examples, each with the adjective clause shown in italics:

> He telephoned the woman *who hired him to photograph her children.*

Who is the relative pronoun. Its antecedent is *the woman.*

> Students *whose last names begin with L–R* will take the examination in Room 102.

Whose is the relative pronoun. Its antecedent is *Students.*

> Rising above the treetops is the tower of Baker Library, *which overlooks the green.*

Which is the relative pronoun. Its antecedent is *Baker Library.*

> Things *that go bump in the night* can be scary.

That is the relative pronoun. Its antecedent is *Things.*

Adjective Clauses and Commas

Use commas to set off an adjective clause when it is **nonrestrictive**—that is, when it neither identifies nor restricts the meaning of its headword. (The headword of an adjective clause is the same as the antecedent of the relative pronoun.) Consider this sentence:

> Shirley Temple, *who made her name as a child movie actress in the 1930s,* earned more than a million dollars by the age of ten.

Here the adjective clause does not restrict the meaning of its headword, *Shirley Temple*. Since Shirley Temple is already identified by her name, the adjective clause is nonrestrictive, not essential. Without the adjective clause some details would be lacking, but the meaning of the sentence would be basically unchanged:

> Shirley Temple earned more than a million dollars by the age of ten.

But consider this sentence:

> Anyone *who earns more than a million dollars by the age of ten* is truly extraordinary.

Here the adjective clause is **restrictive**; it restricts, or limits, the meaning of its headword, *Anyone*. Without the adjective clause, the sentence would say:

> Anyone is truly extraordinary.

Since a restrictive clause is essential to the meaning of its headword, it must not be set off or cut off from that headword by any commas. (For an exercise on punctuating restrictive and nonrestrictive clauses and phrases, see p. 237.)

Placing Adjective Clauses

An adjective clause should normally be placed right after the antecedent of the relative pronoun. If you put any words between the antecedent and the relative pronoun, you must be sure that the connection between the two is clear:

> The coach asked to see the children in the Recreation Program *who wanted to play baseball.*

Because *who* refers to persons, the adjective clause clearly modifies *children,* not *Program.* But if the reader cannot readily connect the relative pronoun with its antecedent, the sentence will be unclear:

> Martin Luther King, Jr., one of the leaders of the civil-rights movement *who won the Nobel Peace Prize in 1964,* was assassinated in 1968.

Does *who* refer to *Martin Luther King* or to *leaders?* Since it could refer to *leaders,* the reader cannot definitely connect it to *Martin Luther King,* its true antecedent. You can clarify a sentence like this by using the relative pronoun right after its antecedent as well as further on:

> Martin Luther King, who was one of the leaders of the civil-rights movement and who won the Nobel Peace Prize in 1964, was assassinated in 1968.

6.5 Adverb Clauses

Like an ordinary adverb, an **adverb clause** can modify a word, a phrase, or an entire clause:

> Vexed *because he could not have his way,* Rex walked out.

The adverb clause modifies the word *Vexed,* telling why.

> Driving west *as the sun was setting,* I had to squint.

The adverb clause modifies the phrase *Driving west,* telling when.

> *After the volcano erupted,* the sky became dark.

The adverb clause modifies the clause *the sky became dark,* telling when.

Adverb Clauses and Main Clauses

Directly or indirectly, an adverb clause is always subordinate to the main clause in a sentence:

ADVERB CLAUSE	MAIN CLAUSE
Though the front door was locked,	I managed to climb in through a window.

MAIN CLAUSE	ADVERB CLAUSE
But a policeman saw me	*as I was entering the house.*

By subordinating one clause to another, you can indicate which of two statements is more important than the other. The more important statement is in the main clause.

Choosing Subordinators

An adverb clause always begins with a **subordinator,** a word or phrase that subordinates the clause to whatever it modifies. The subordinator helps to signal the relation between the two. Here are the principal relations and the subordinators that indicate them:

1. Time, indicated by *after, as, as soon as, as long as, before, since, ever since, until, when, while;*

2. Causality, indicated by *because, since;*

3. Concession and contrast, indicated by *although, even though, though, whereas, while;*

4. Condition, indicated by *if, as if, as though, provided that, unless;*

5. Purpose, indicated by *so that, in order that, lest;*

6. Place, indicated by *where;*

7. Result, indicated by *so that, so . . . that* (as in *I was so bored that I walked out*);

8. General possibility, indicated by *whatever, whenever, wherever, whoever, whichever, however;*

9. Comparison, indicated by *than.*

Since *as* can mean *while,* you should avoid using it to mean *because;* if you use it in that way, your sentence may be unclear:

> WEAK: As the roof leaked, no one was comfortable.
> REVISED: Because the roof leaked, no one was comfortable.

Name_____ Date_____

Exercise 1.   Recognizing and Using Noun Clauses

Part A.   In each of the following sentences, underline the noun clause. Then in the blank at right indicate how it is used: as a subject (*S*), as the object of a verb (*O*), as the object of a preposition (*OP*), or as a predicate noun (*PRED N*).

EXAMPLE

<u>Whatever a president says about foreign affairs</u> gets worldwide attention.   <u>S</u>

1. Whoever has the necessary qualifications will be given an interview.   _____

2. One question still to be answered is how the new construction will be financed.   _____

3. That no one was injured in the accident is incredible.   _____

4. On opening day the owners will give free baskets of fresh fruit to whoever makes a purchase totaling twenty or more dollars.   _____

5. What the dying man said to the priest can never be known.   _____

6. Have you ever wished that you could fly?   _____

7. The guide showed us where the royal fugitive hid for two months.   _____

8. The recommendation of the mediator is that a compromise be reached.   _____

9. Doctors usually know when their patients are frightened.   _____

10. Inspectors investigating the accident now wonder whether the pilot lost contact with the control tower.   _____

Part B. Combine the sentences in each of the following pairs by changing one of them into a noun clause beginning with the word given in parentheses.

EXAMPLE

Sylvia did something. (what)
It amazed me.

What Sylvia did amazed me.

1. A certain type of person will enjoy reading *Anglers' Luck.*
   The person likes to fish. (whoever)

2. Oldtimers in the village believe something.
   The inn is haunted. (that)

3. Our objection is something.
   The proposed street lights are too expensive. (that)

4. Senators always wonder something.
   How will the voters react to an increase in taxes? (how)

5. A panel of the country's leading architects has offered a $10,000 prize to a certain person.
   The person designs the most energy-efficient home possible. (whoever)

Name_____ Date_____

Exercise 2.   Recognizing and Using Adjective Clauses

Part A.   In each of the following sentences, underline the adjective clause. Then circle the relative pronoun and draw an arrow to its antecedent.

EXAMPLE

Harry was injured by a brick (that) fell from a roof.

1. My father, who rarely loses his temper, almost exploded with rage.

2. The injured man did not even notice the flowers that we brought him.

3. Applicants whose parents attended the university receive preferential treatment.

4. The pilot whale, which frequents the Arctic, is actually a large dolphin.

5. Any man that voted for O'Malley in the last election is no friend of mine.

6. Students who fail one or more courses are not eligible for a place on the varsity.

7. The attorney general will prosecute individuals and companies that break the law prohibiting the dumping of poisonous wastes in unprotected areas.

8. The president would prefer to spend the weekend in a place where reporters won't swamp him with questions.

9. According to legend, Helen of Troy, over whom the Greeks and Trojans waged a long and bitter war, was the most beautiful woman in the world.

10. The convention will be held in the Greenspot Hotel, which is two blocks west of the bus depot.

Part B. Combine the sentences in each of the following pairs by changing one of them into an adjective clause.

EXAMPLE

On his seventieth birthday, President Reagan was given a flag. The flag was flown over the Capitol during his inauguration.

On his seventieth birthday, President Reagan was given a flag that was flown over the Capitol during his inauguration.

1. The Canada goose used to inhabit wild, desolate areas.
   The Canada goose now frequents suburbia.

2. College coaches across the country have been talking to Roger Fastback.
   Roger Fastback has set new records for passing and running in high school football.

3. Under the rationing plan, certain motorists could buy gas on Tuesdays, Thursdays, and Saturdays.
   Those motorists' license plates end in an odd number.

4. Food inspectors have closed two restaurants.
   The restaurants served tainted shellfish.

5. Betty White is one official.
   All the players respect this official.

Name _____ Date _____

Exercise 3.   Recognizing and Using Adverb Clauses

Part A.   In each of the following sentences, underline the adverb clause and circle the subordinator.

EXAMPLE

Some dog in the neighborhood howls (whenever) the fire alarm goes off.

1. Unless the fans become orderly, the game will be forfeited to the visiting team.

2. You will strain your eyes if you continue to read in the dark.

3. The major characters in the novel are less interesting than the minor ones are.

4. People dare not drink unbottled water because the wells have become polluted.

5. The committee has simplified the line of command so that its operations will speed up.

6. As soon as the explorer entered the ancient tomb, he spotted a gold mask on the dirt floor.

7. The supply of coal may have to be rationed before the energy crisis ends.

8. During each alert the trainees sprint for the planes as though their lives were at stake.

9. The weather is so hot that few venture outdoors between 11 A.M. and 2 P.M.

10. Even after sixty performances, the leading man studies his lines before he goes onstage.

Part B. Combine the sentences in each of the following pairs by changing one of them into an adverb clause.

EXAMPLE

The concert will begin at a certain time.
The president is seated at this time.

The concert will begin when the president is seated.

1. Motorists have been advised not to drive.
   The roads are icy.

2. Suppose the foundation is strong.
   Then the rest of the building will stand.

3. Roger Green has had no experience in local or state politics.
   He intends to seek election to the Senate.

4. The crew members checked their gear three times for a certain purpose.
   Nothing would malfunction during the mission.

5. The boxer jumped out of the ring at a certain time.
   He saw his opponent at that time.

6.6   Making Comparisons Complete   *comp*

To be complete, a comparison may require an adverb clause, as in the following example:

> The company earned less in 1980 *than it did in 1979.*

You should normally write out a comparison in full. The omission of a word or words can result in puzzling or even illogical statements. For example:

> PUZZLING: A director usually thinks more about the plot of a script than the actors.

Does this mean that a director thinks more about the plot than about the actors, or more about the plot than the actors think about it? The sentence should tell us which:

> A director usually thinks more about the plot of a script *than the actors do.*

Here is another example:

> ILLOGICAL: Passenger trains in Japan run much faster than the United States.

This sentence seems to compare trains with the United States. It should compare trains with trains or with some other form of transportation:

> Passenger trains in Japan run much faster *than trains in the United States do.*

You can use *those* instead of *trains,* and you can omit the final *do* as long as the sentence is clear without it:

> Passenger trains in Japan run much faster *than those in the United States.*

When you compare one item with others in its class, you must use *other* or *else* with the second item:

> Though her own part was small, Cheryl knew the play better than anyone in the cast.
> REVISED: Though her own part was small, Cheryl knew the play better *than anyone else in the cast.*

6.7   Using Two or More Subordinate Clauses

A sentence can have more than one subordinate clause. Consider these examples:

1. When Priscilla was hit by a brick that fell from a roof, her mother called an ambulance.

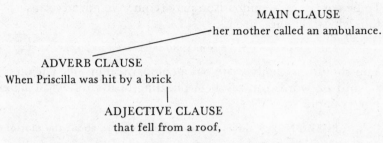

MAIN CLAUSE
her mother called an ambulance.

ADVERB CLAUSE
When Priscilla was hit by a brick

ADJECTIVE CLAUSE
that fell from a roof,

2. Jeff decided that he would order a tuna-fish sandwich, which was the cheapest thing on the menu.

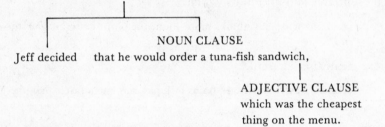

MAIN CLAUSE

NOUN CLAUSE
Jeff decided   that he would order a tuna-fish sandwich,

ADJECTIVE CLAUSE
which was the cheapest
thing on the menu.

3. Since the part that I needed was no longer available from the factory, I had to get it from a junk dealer.

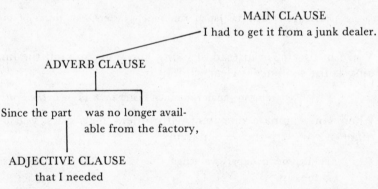

MAIN CLAUSE
I had to get it from a junk dealer.

ADVERB CLAUSE

Since the part   was no longer available from the factory,

ADJECTIVE CLAUSE
that I needed

4. Where the thieves hid the money is a question that the police are still trying to answer.

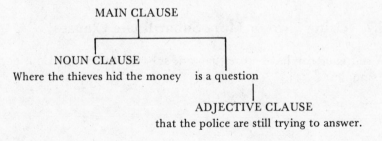

MAIN CLAUSE

NOUN CLAUSE
Where the thieves hid the money   is a question

ADJECTIVE CLAUSE
that the police are still trying to answer.

Name _____ Date _____

Exercise 4.   Writing Comparisons

Each of the following sentences makes a comparison. If the comparison is mishandled, rewrite the sentence, using an adverb clause or whatever else is needed to make the comparison clear and complete. If a sentence is correct as it stands, write *Correct*.

EXAMPLE

The pond is as polluted as three years ago.

The pond is as polluted as it was three years ago.

1. The population of London is larger than Boston.

2. Paula, a center, is more aggressive than any player on her team.

3. The plot of Brant's second novel is more complicated than his first.

4. Joe likes the family's new car more than his wife.

5. The musicians performed better in the second half of the program than the first.

6. The temperature in Nome is usually lower than Buffalo.

7. The acoustics in the new auditorium are not so good as those in the old one.

8. Albert Cheque has as many bank accounts in Switzerland as the United States.

9. Madame Bovary was less worried about her husband than her lover.

10. The wingspan of the new X-82 fighter plane is shorter than the X-70.

Name _____ Date _____

Exercise 5.   Review: Using More Than One Subordinate Clause

Combine the sentences in each of the following sets by using the italicized sentence as a main clause and the other sentences as subordinate clauses.

EXAMPLE

Customers have complained for a certain reason.
The milk turned out to be sour.
They bought the milk on Saturday.

Customers have complained because the milk that they bought on Saturday turned out to be sour.

1. John entered the church at a certain time.
   He decided something at the same time.
   He would not stay for the sermon.

2. Sarah was enjoying her retirement.
   She answered an advertisement.
   The advertisement listed two openings for accountants.

3. A certain type of person likes roller coasters of a certain kind.
   These roller coasters defy gravity.
   This type of person will want to take a ride on the Flying Dragon.

4. Every package brought to the prison is thoroughly inspected.
   How did the prisoners manage to get twenty sticks of dynamite?
   No one can figure that out.

5. Thomas Edison began making movies in 1893.
   But the first major American film was created by Edwin S. Porter.
   Porter directed *The Great Train Robbery* in 1903.

6. This film was only eight minutes long.
   But it strongly influenced the development of movie-making.
   It introduced new devices such as the intercutting of scenes.

Name _____ Date _____

Exercise 5, *continued*

7. Charlie Chaplin got his start in the slapstick comedies of Mack Sennett.
   Then Chaplin invented the tramp character.
   This character brought him international fame.

8. The sensational appearance of *The Jazz Singer* in 1927 proved something.
   Talking movies could be successfully made.
   The movie-making industry was transformed.

9. Studios had previously cared only about the way actors looked and moved.
   They now wanted actors of a certain kind.
   Actors of this kind could speak effectively.

10. Television challenged the popularity of movies after World War II.
    The movie industry responded with the Cinerama system.
    This system uses three interlocked projectors and a wide curving screen.

7

USING COORDINATION AND SUBORDINATION TOGETHER

Once you have learned how to use coordination and subordination separately, you can use them together to arrange all parts of a sentence according to their relative importance. Consider this example:

> I was hot and tired, but I kept on pedaling because I wanted to reach Phoenix, where my grandparents would give me a good dinner and a bed for the night.

INDEPENDENT (COORDINATE) CLAUSES

COORDINATE ADJECTIVES

I was hot and tired,   but I kept on pedaling

SUBORDINATE CLAUSE
because I wanted to
reach Phoenix,

SUBORDINATE CLAUSE
where my grandparents would
give me

COORDINATE PHRASES

a good dinner and a bed for the night.

This sentence coordinates items of equal importance and subordinates less important items to more important ones. It coordinates the two independent clauses, the words *hot* and *tired,* and the phrases *a good dinner* and *a bed for the night;* it subordinates the *because* clause to the clause about pedaling, and it subordinates the *where* clause to the *because* clause. Thus subordination and coordination work together.

Name _____ Date _____

Exercise.   Using Coordination and Subordination Together

This exercise tests your ability to use coordination and subordination together. If you don't already know how to use them separately, you should study the chapter on coordination (pp. 69–87) and the chapter on subordination (pp. 99–117) before you begin this exercise. Using coordination and subordination together, make one sentence from each of the following sets of sentences. Include all the information given, but feel free to change the wording or arrangement of the sentences.

EXAMPLE

I was hot.
I was tired.
I kept pedaling.
I wanted to reach Phoenix.
There my grandparents would give me a good dinner.
They would also give me a bed for the night.

I was hot and tired, but I kept on pedaling because I wanted to reach Phoenix, where my grandparents would give me a good dinner and a bed for the night.

1. The Spaniards came to the region of New Mexico in the early sixteenth century.
    Then they explored the region.
    They conquered the Pueblo Indians.
    They founded Santa Fe.
    Santa Fe is now the state capital.

2. The Indians revolted in 1680.
   They drove the Spanish out of the region.
   The Spanish soon reconquered it.

3. The region became a Mexican province in 1821.
   Then the Republic of Texas wanted to move its western bound-
   ary to the Rio Grande.
   The Rio Grande flows through New Mexico.
   Texas failed to conquer the region.

4. During the Mexican War, United States forces occupied the region.
   They ruled it with a military government.
   It was ceded to the United States under the Treaty of Guadalupe
   Hidalgo.
   That treaty ended the war.

Name _____ Date _____

Exercise, *continued*

5. In 1906 Congress voted something.
    The territories of New Mexico and Arizona could become one state—on one condition.
    A majority of the voters in each territory had to approve the union.
    A majority of the Arizona voters opposed the proposal.
    The territorial status of New Mexico remained unchanged until 1912.
    At that time New Mexico was admitted to the Union as a state.

8

COMPLETE SENTENCES
AND
SENTENCE FRAGMENTS

Complete sentences convey or help to convey what most readers expect to find in good writing: complete thoughts. Sentence fragments do just the opposite. Unless skillfully used, they convey the impression that the writer's thoughts are fragmentary or incomplete.

8.1   What Is a Sentence Fragment?

A sentence fragment is a part of a sentence punctuated as if it were a whole one. Here are some examples:

> Often a subordinate clause or a phrase.†
> Separated from its base sentence by a period.
> Sometimes a word group lacking a subject or a complete predicate.
> Seldom fully intelligible by itself.
> To be avoided in most college writing.

8.2   What's Wrong with Sentence Fragments?

You probably write fragments like those in the preceding examples when taking notes during a lecture, making a list of things to do, or planning an essay. You see fragments in advertisements, newspaper headlines, and passages of dialogue in plays, short stories, and novels. And you regularly hear and use fragments when talking with others. Here are some more examples:

> Buy Venus Shampoo. Right away! To make you feel like a goddess!
> Have to run. See you later.
> 'Bye for now!

†Normally in this book nonstandard constructions used for illustration are marked with a star. However, in this chapter sentence fragments are not starred because, as the text points out, they may be acceptable under certain special circumstances.

Though fragments like these are common in speech and writing, you should avoid them in your essays. They tend to make a piece of writing look disorganized, and for that reason they are generally not accepted in college essays, formal reports, and business letters. In any case, you should not attempt to use a sentence fragment until you have clearly and consistently demonstrated your ability to write complete sentences.

8.3 Spotting and Correcting Sentence Fragments *frag*

In order to spot and correct sentence fragments, you will need to develop a reliable "sentence sense"—the ability to distinguish between complete sentences and fragments. To develop this ability, you can ask certain questions.

1. Does the "sentence" sound like a sentence? One way to distinguish between a sentence and a fragment is to listen to the difference between them. If you read your own sentences aloud and let your voice fall with each period, you may be able to hear which "sentences" are really nonsentences.

2. Does the "sentence" have a subject?

> FRAGMENT: Is seldom fully intelligible by itself.
> REVISED: A fragment is seldom fully intelligible by itself.

> FRAGMENT: Stretched upward as if to touch the clouds.
> REVISED: The green branches stretched upward as if to touch the clouds.

3. Does the "sentence" have a verb of suitable form in the predicate?

> FRAGMENT: He working hard to support his sister's family.
> REVISED: He has been working hard to support his sister's family.

A participle, such as *working,* cannot serve by itself as the verb in a sentence. It must be part of a verb phrase—in this case, *has been working.*

4. Does the "sentence" consist of a word group separated from its base sentence by a period? The word group will usually be one of those listed here.

> 1. A prepositional phrase:
>
>> BASE SENTENCE: The Republican candidate appeared at the ground-breaking ceremony.
>> FRAGMENT: Along with a television crew and three newspaper reporters.
>> REVISED SENTENCE: The Republican candidate appeared at the ground-breaking ceremony along with a television crew and three newspaper reporters.

126

2. A participle phrase:

> BASE SENTENCE: During her convalescence Beth liked to watch the snowflakes.
> FRAGMENT: Riding the wind and swirling about like tiny, weightless diamonds.
> REVISED SENTENCE: During her convalescence Beth liked to watch the snowflakes riding the wind and swirling about like tiny, weightless diamonds.

3. An infinitive phrase:

> BASE SENTENCE: Frank has been going to night school since February.
> FRAGMENT: To learn accounting.
> REVISED SENTENCE: Frank has been going to night school since February to learn accounting.

4. An appositive:

> BASE SENTENCE: A jealous husband shot and killed Stanford White.
> FRAGMENT: A leading American architect in the early twentieth century.
> REVISED SENTENCE: A jealous husband shot and killed Stanford White, a leading American architect in the early twentieth century.

5. An adverb clause (one beginning with a subordinator, such as *although, because, if, when, since,* or *so that*):

> BASE SENTENCE: Thousands died in Ireland.
> FRAGMENT: When a blight struck the potato crop there in the 1840s.
> REVISED SENTENCE: Thousands died in Ireland when a blight struck the potato crop there in the 1840s.

6. An adjective clause (one usually beginning with a relative pronoun, such as *who, whose, which, that, where,* or *when*):

> BASE SENTENCE: My grandfather is proud of a banjo clock.
> FRAGMENT: Which he restored to mint condition after finding it in a junk shop.
> REVISED SENTENCE: My grandfather is proud of a banjo clock which he restored to mint condition after finding it in a junk shop.

7. A noun and an adjective clause:

> BASE SENTENCE: Galveston, Texas, has a plaque to commemorate Leroy Colombo.
> FRAGMENT: A lifeguard who during his life saved 907 people from drowning off Galveston Island.
> REVISED SENTENCE: Galveston, Texas, has a plaque to commemorate Leroy Colombo, a lifeguard who during his life saved 907 people from drowning off Galveston Island.

8. A noun clause:

BASE SENTENCE: I suddenly remembered.
FRAGMENT: That I had left the keys in the pocket of my other coat.
REVISED SENTENCE: I suddenly remembered that I had left the keys in the pocket of my other coat.

FRAGMENT: What I want.
FRAGMENT: Is a pickup truck.
REVISED: What I want is a pickup truck.

Name _____ Date _____

Exercise 1. Supplying Subjects and Verbs of Suitable Form

Each of the following may be a fragment, lacking either a subject or a verb of suitable form in the predicate. Where you find a fragment, write *Fragment* in the blank at right. Then turn the word group into a sentence by supplying a subject or changing the form of the verb. When you find a complete sentence, write *Sentence*.

EXAMPLE

Have been reading the novels of Balzac this term. *Fragment*

The students in French 302 have been reading the novels of Balzac this term.

1. Settlers from as far away as Australia been moving into the territory for the past two years. _____

2. Is bordered on the north by Canada and on the south by Mexico. _____

3. Thoroughly confused every student in Philosophy 101. _____

4. They unwilling to support the plan. _____

5. Some geological changes happening very quickly. _____

6. Crumbled into dust at a touch. _____

7. Saw an enormous ice-dammed glacial lake in western Montana. _____

8. The lot been vacant for months. _____

9. She listened with patience and understanding. _____

10. Was appalled by the flimsiness of the evidence. _____

Name_____ Date _____

Exercise 2.   Connecting Phrases with Base Sentences

Each of the following may include a phrase separated from its base sentence by a period. Where you find this error, circle the letter of the fragmented phrase, and in the blank at right identify it if you can—as a prepositional phrase (*PREP*), a participle phrase (*PART*), an infinitive phrase (*INF*), or an appositive (*APP*). Then rewrite the sentence, correcting the punctuation to eliminate the fragment. If an entry consists of two complete sentences, write *Correct*.

EXAMPLE

   (a)   After a series of defeats, the soldiers wanted a   *app* new leader.

   (b)   A brave and brilliant strategist.

After a series of defeats, the soldiers wanted a new leader, a brave and brilliant strategist.

1. (a)   All mammals breathe about 200 billion times.   _____
    (b)   During their lives.

2. (a)   Everyone cheered for Diana.   _____
    (b)   The beautiful bride of Prince Charles.

3. (a)   The little girl perched on the balcony rail.   _____
    (b)   To see the circus parade.

4. (a)   Jamie packed his bags and left for school.   _____
    (b)   Without a backward glance.

5. (a) Singing its strangely beautiful song. _____
   (b) The humpback whale swims lazily through the great oceans.

6. (a) With a malicious gleam in her eye. _____
   (b) The headmistress announced that the school vacation would be shortened.

7. (a) In 1931 Boris Karloff was paid $125 a week. _____
   (b) For playing the role of the monster in the movie *Frankenstein*.

8. (a) Bryce learned never to complain. _____
   (b) But he always listened to the complaints of others.

9. (a) Pascal was haunted by the fear of an abyss. _____
   (b) A bottomless, inescapable pit of nonbeing.

10. (a) I found her outside. _____
    (b) She was sitting on a bench.

Name _____ Date _____

Exercise 3.   Connecting Subordinate Clauses with Base Sentences

Each of the following may include a subordinate clause separated from its base sentence by a period. Where you find this error, circle the letter of the fragmented clause, and in the blank at right identify it if you can—as an adverb clause (*ADV*), an adjective clause (*ADJ*), or a noun clause (*N*). Then rewrite the sentence, correcting the punctuation to eliminate the fragment. If an entry consists entirely of complete sentences, write *Correct.*

EXAMPLE

(a)   I watched the surface of the stream.   *ADV*
(b)   While I waited tensely for a fish to strike and begin the duel.

I watched the surface of the stream while I waited tensely for a fish to strike and begin the duel.

1. (a)   I was always astonished by my grandmother's   _____
   ability to retrieve old records, toys, and pictures
   from the attic.
   (b)   Which the rest of the family considered an impenetrable maze.

2. (a)   Every year the Nutley Chapter of the Millard   _____
   Fillmore Society awards a scholarship to a high
   school student.
   (b)   Who has an average of less than C.

3. (a) Though there are some 7.5 million differences in color. _____
   (b) We normally "see" only about two dozen different shades.

4. (a) The child who approaches learning as problem-solving has an advantage. _____
   (b) He or she will ultimately learn more than the child who sees learning as second-guessing the teacher.

5. (a) Since we can't control government spending, the hydrogen bomb, or terrorism in the Middle East. _____
   (b) We should try at least to control our appetites.

6. (a) Caesar was fifty-two and Cleopatra was twenty-one. _____
   (b) When they were lovers.

8. Complete Sentences and Sentence Fragments

Name _____ Date _____

Exercise 3, *continued*

7. (a)   All ten of the world's coldest cities are in the   _____
         Soviet Union.
   (b)   Which extends into the Arctic.

8. (a)   There is never any fat on a shark steak.   _____
   (b)   Because the shark stores all its fat in its liver.

9. (a)   Darwin stressed the fecundity of organisms in   _____
         explaining the process of natural selection.
   (b)   The term "survival of the fittest" is a misleading
         phrase.

10. (a)   I suspected.   _____
    (b)   That the diamond was a fake.

Name _____ Date _____

Exercise 4.   Review: Recognizing and Correcting Sentence Fragments

Each of the following may include a fragment of some sort. Where you find a fragment, circle the letter of the fragment, and in the blank at right identify it if you can, using the appropriate designation as specified in exercise 2 (p. 131) and exercise 3 (p. 133). Then rewrite the sentence, correcting the punctuation to eliminate the fragment. If an entry consists of two complete sentences, write *Correct*.

EXAMPLE

(a)   Because of the groundwater in the region, you should check the basement of any house that interests you.   *PREP*

(b)   Before making a firm offer to buy it.

Because of the groundwater in the region, you should check the basement of any house that interests you before making a firm offer to buy it.

1.   (a)   Fred combed the college catalogs.   _____
     (b)   Searching for courses in biochemistry.

2.   (a)   From the time of the Vikings.   _____
     (b)   Denmark has celebrated the longest day of the year with bonfires along its coastlines.

3.   (a)   The new rule infuriated Stimson.   _____
     (b)   Who quit the team in protest.

4. (a) George was chosen Player of the Year.   _____
   (b) Then he became the world's greatest egomaniac.

5. (a) After its capture by the Turks in 1458.   _____
   (b) Athens nearly disappeared from the view of the
       Western world.

6. (a) Barbara wondered.   _____
   (b) What she could do.

7. (a) Though Antarctica has no indigenous human   _____
       population.
   (b) The Arctic has supported human life for cen-
       turies.

8. (a) Strong analgesics, such as opium, morphine and   _____
       heroin, should be used cautiously.
   (b) They should be taken only under the supervision
       of a physician.

9. (a) The exhausted climbers struggled up the north   _____
       slope.
   (b) To reach a camping spot before nightfall.

10. (a) They spent each summer in Ogunquit.   _____
    (b) A lovely old town on the seacoast of Maine.

Name _____ Date _____

Exercise 5. Recognizing and Correcting Sentence Fragments in a Passage

The following passage is a rewritten version of a paragraph in Henry Gleitman's *Psychology*. In rewriting Gleitman's paragraph, we have deliberately introduced several sentence fragments. Correct the punctuation to remove them, writing out just the segments that need correcting.

EXAMPLE

line 2: life and that

1   . . . Imprinting in birds [is] a kind of learning that occurs
2   very early in life. And that provides the basis for the chick's at-
3   tachment to its mother. When a newly hatched duckling is first
4   exposed to a moving stimulus. It will approach and follow the
5   stimulus as soon as it is able to walk (at about twelve hours af-
6   ter hatching). If the chick follows the object for as little as ten
7   minutes. An attachment is formed; the bird is imprinted. In
8   nature, the moving stimulus is the duckling's mother and all is
9   well. But in the laboratory it need not be. The duckling may be
10   exposed. To a wooden duck on wheels. Or to a rectangle sliding
11   back and forth behind a glass window, or even to Konrad Lorenz'
12   booted legs. In each case the result is the same. The duckling be-
13   comes imprinted on the wooden duck or the rectangle or Lorenz;
14   it follows these objects as if they were its mother. Uttering pit-
15   eous distress calls. Whenever they are not nearby. . . . Imprinting
16   is hard to reverse. The attachment remains. Despite the fact that
17   the inanimate objects give neither food nor comfort. The real
18   mother may quack enticingly so as to woo her lost offspring back,
19   but to no avail; the imprinted duckling continues to follow
20   Lorenz.

9

USING
PRONOUNS

A **pronoun** is a word that commonly takes the place of a noun or noun phrase that has already been used:

> Seth forgot where *he* had left his coat.

The pronoun *he* takes the place of *Seth,* a noun.

> The town manager said that *she* would personally supervise the clean-up project.

The pronoun *she* takes the place of *The town manager,* a noun phrase.

A pronoun can also take the place of a whole clause or sentence that has already been used:

> With the bases loaded in the bottom of the ninth, Reggie Jackson hit the ball into the right-field stands. *That* ended the game.

9.1 Pronouns and Antecedents

As already stated in "Relative Pronouns and Antecedents," p. 100, the word or word group that a pronoun refers to is called the **antecedent** of the pronoun. In the preceding examples, the antecedent of *he* is *Seth,* the antecedent of *she* is *The town manager,* and the antecedent of *That* is the whole sentence about Reggie Jackson. Now consider another example:

> A big crowd gathered to see the president, *who* arrived just after noon.

The antecedent of *who* is *the president.* You may have recognized *who* as a relative pronoun, a pronoun that introduces an adjective clause.

9.2 Pronouns That Have No Antecedent

Pronouns may be definite or indefinite. A pronoun that normally requires an antecedent is called **definite** because it gets a well-defined meaning from the antecedent. But some pronouns have no antecedent, and others may sometimes be used without one. Compare these two sentences:

> Bankers in Chicago have not decided whether *they* will lower the interest rate to 15 percent.
> Inflation affects *everyone.*

In the first sentence, *they* is a definite pronoun, referring to *Bankers in Chicago.* In the second sentence, *everyone* is an **indefinite** pronoun; it has no antecedent, but its meaning is clear without one. (For a complete list of indefinite pronouns, see p. 145.)

9.3 Pronoun Reference *pn ref*

Clear Reference

A pronoun that needs an antecedent should clearly refer to one. The meaning of a definite pronoun is clear when readers can readily identify its antecedent. Here are some examples of clear reference:

> Val was irritated by the old alarm clock. *Its* loud ticking kept *her* awake for much of the night.

Its clearly refers to *the old alarm clock,* and *her* to *Val.*

> Ike is building a house with solar panels on the roof. *These* will help *him* control *his* heating costs.

These refers to *panels; him* and *his* refer to *Ike.*

> The dean has proposed a no-cut policy for freshmen, but if adopted, *it* will be hard to enforce.

It clearly refers to *a no-cut policy for freshmen.*

Unclear Reference

The meaning of a definite pronoun is unclear when readers find no antecedent for it:

> There is considerable opposition to the new thirty-minute limit on downtown parking. *They* want a sixty-minute limit.

In this case, *they* has no antecedent. To clarify the sentence, you must either supply an antecedent or replace the pronoun with a noun:

> Many people oppose the new thirty-minute limit on downtown parking. They want a sixty-minute limit. [or] There is considerable opposition to

the new thirty-minute limit on downtown parking. Many people want a sixty-minute limit.

The meaning of a definite pronoun is also unclear when it has two or more possible antecedents:

The new owners have made many improvements, including a new swimming pool, a roof garden, two tennis courts, and a comfortable lounge. They hope *this* will attract guests.

The meaning of *this* is unclear. *This* may refer either to *a comfortable lounge* or to all of the improvements. To clarify the second sentence, you should replace *this* with a noun or noun phrase:

They hope the lounge will attract guests. [or] They hope all these improvements will attract guests.

9.4 Making Pronouns and Antecedents Agree *pn agr*

Gender

Some pronouns indicate **gender:** they may be masculine (for example, *he*), feminine (*she*), or neuter (*it*). The gender of a pronoun should match the gender of its antecedent:

Sally said that *she* liked *her* physics course.
The engine is guaranteed to run well if *it* is properly lubricated.
Betty told Mike that *she* would treat *him* to a pizza.
Betty told Mike that *he* should treat *her* to a pizza.

Pronouns with Antecedents of Unspecified Gender

When the antecedent of a pronoun is a singular noun that could be either masculine or feminine, writers have customarily used a masculine pronoun:

A judge should reach *his* verdict only after weighing all of the evidence carefully.

But this construction implies that all judges are male. If the antecedent could be masculine or feminine, your sentence should recognize that fact. You can use a pair of pronouns linked by *or:*

A judge should reach *his* or *her* verdict only after weighing all of the evidence carefully.

To avoid an accumulation of double pronouns, you can often make the antecedent plural and use a plural pronoun, which does not indicate gender:

Judges should reach *their* verdicts only after weighing all of the evidence carefully.

Alternatively, you can sometimes substitute a construction that eliminates pronouns:

A judge should reach a verdict only after weighing all of the evidence carefully.

Number

All pronouns that require antecedents are either singular (for example, *he*) or plural (*they*). A pronoun is singular if it refers to one person or thing, and plural if it refers to more than one. A singular antecedent calls for a singular pronoun; a plural antecedent calls for a plural pronoun:

> The river is eroding *its* banks.
> The rivers are eroding *their* banks.
>
> The boy grinned when *he* saw the pie.
> The boys groaned when *they* saw the spinach.

Problems with Number

Antecedents of the following kinds are problem cases—hard to classify as either singular or plural. We suggest that you treat them as indicated.

1. Two or more nouns or pronouns joined by *and* are usually plural:

> Sam and Sharon reached home before *their* mother did.
> The boys and girls left *their* coats in the hall.

Whether the nouns joined by *and* are singular or plural, two or more of them make a plural antecedent.

2. When two nouns are joined by *or* or *nor,* the pronoun normally agrees with the second:

> Either John or Frank had left *his* boots behind.
> Neither Frank nor the children had remembered *their* boots.

3. A noun or pronoun followed by a prepositional phrase is treated as if it stood by itself:

> By evening the bouquet of wild flowers had lost *its* scent.

The pronoun agrees with *bouquet,* just as it would if the wild flowers were not mentioned and the sentence read *By evening the bouquet had lost its scent.*

> Five men in the platoon forgot *their* helmets.

The pronoun agrees with *men.*

4. Collective nouns—nouns referring to a group—can be singular or plural, depending on the context in which they are used:

> The crowd gradually forgot *its* angry mood.
> After the speech the crowd dispersed to *their* cars.

5. Some indefinite pronouns are singular, some are plural, and some can be either singular or plural:

ALWAYS SINGULAR

anybody	either	one
anyone	neither	another
anything	nobody	somebody
each	none	someone
each one	no one	something
everybody	nothing	whatever
everyone		whichever
everything		whoever

ALWAYS PLURAL

both   few   others   several

SOMETIMES SINGULAR AND SOMETIMES PLURAL

all   many   some

any   most

Pronouns in the first group are always singular:

> Everything was in *its* place.
>
> Everyone at the meeting voiced *his* or *her* opinion.

Pronouns in the second group are always plural:

> Others wanted *their* plan adopted.

The number of a pronoun in the third group depends on the number of the word or phrase to which it refers:

> Some of the grass has lost *its* color.
>
> Some of the flowers had lost *their* petals.
>
> Many of the companies have pension plans for *their* employees.
>
> Many a woman finds that marriage interferes with *her* career.

6. The number of a relative pronoun depends on the number of its antecedent:

> Customers who fail to pay *their* bills within thirty days are liable for interest charges.
>
> A customer who fails to pay *his* or *her* bill within thirty days is liable for interest charges.

9.5 Pronoun Case *pn ca*

The **case** of a pronoun is the form it takes as determined by its role in a sentence—the grammatical function that it serves. Some of the ways in which a pronoun can be used are shown in the following examples:

> Bob no longer complains about modern poetry. Now *he* likes it.

He is the subject of the verb *likes*.

The complexities of some poems no longer trouble *him*.

Him is the object of the verb *trouble*.

In fact, he welcomes the challenge to *his* intelligence.

His indicates possession.

A big crowd gathered to see the president, *who* arrived just after noon.

Who is the subject of the verb *arrived*.

The crowd waited eagerly to see the president, *whose* plane had been delayed.

Whose indicates possession.

The townspeople cheered the president, for *whom* they had been waiting over an hour.

Whom is the object of the preposition *for*.
Here are the case forms of all pronouns that have them.

CASE FORMS OF PRONOUNS

PERSONAL PRONOUNS

	I	He	She	It	We	You	They
Subject case	I	he	she	it	we	you	they
Object case	me	him	her	it	us	you	them
Possessive case	my, mine	his	her, hers	its	our, ours	your, yours	their, theirs
Reflexive / emphatic case	myself	him-self	her-self	itself	our-selves	yourself, your-selves	them-selves

PRONOUNS USED IN QUESTIONS AND ADJECTIVE CLAUSES

	Who	Whoever
Subject case	who	whoever
Object case	whom	whomever
Possessive case	whose	

Subject Case

Use the subject case when the pronoun is the subject of a verb:

I rode the roller coaster.
Ellen and *I* played Ping-Pong.
She and *I* share an apartment.

When a compound is used as a subject, a pronoun that is part of the compound must be in the subject case. Do not write *Me and Ellen played Ping-Pong or *Me and her share an apartment.

Object Case

1. Use the object case when the pronoun is the direct or indirect object of a verb:

> The company hired *me*.
> The company hired Louise and *me*.

> The manager showed *me* the apartment.
> The manager showed Louise and *me* the apartment.

When a compound is used as an object, a pronoun that is part of the compound must be in the object case. Do not write *The company hired Louise and I or *The manager showed Louise and I the apartment.

2. Use the object case when the pronoun is the object of a preposition, a word such as *to* or *for:*

> On the sidewalk Peter found a letter addressed to *him*.
> For *them* the news was crushing.

3. Use the object case when the pronoun comes immediately before an infinitive:

> The dean asked *me* to come at noon.
> The dean asked Frank and *me* to come at noon.

Possessive Case

1. Use the possessive case of the pronoun to indicate ownership of an object or close connection with it:

> The guests left *their* boots outside the door.
> *Whose* life is expendable?

2. Use the possessive case when the pronoun comes immediately before a verbal noun:

> Don practiced the piano four hours a day, and the sound of *his* playing got on my nerves.

Do not write *the sound of him playing. When you use an -*ing* word as a verbal noun—as the name of an action—the pronoun before it must be in the possessive case.

Reflexive/Emphatic Case

1. Use the reflexive/emphatic case of the pronoun to indicate a reflexive action—an action affecting the one who performs it:

> She slipped on the ice and hurt *herself*.

2. Use the reflexive/emphatic case of the pronoun to indicate emphasis:

> The mayor *himself* came to the meeting.

Spelling Case Forms Correctly

You can learn to spell pronouns correctly by following these rules:

1. A pronoun in the possessive case should be spelled without an apostrophe:

> *The engine worried me because of it's tendency to stall.
> REVISED: The engine worried me because of its tendency to stall.

It's means *it is*. The possessive pronoun is *its*.

> *My teammates forgot they're uniforms.
> REVISED: My teammates forgot their uniforms.

They're means *they are*. The possessive pronoun is *their*.

> *A stretcher was brought for the player who's leg was broken.
> REVISED: A stretcher was brought for the player whose leg was broken.

Who's means *who is*. The possessive pronoun is *whose*.

2. A pronoun in the reflexive/emphatic case should be spelled by the addition of *-self* or *-selves* to the object case—not to the possessive case:

> *Fred hurt hisself.
> REVISED: Fred hurt himself.

Here *self* is added to the object case (*him*), not to the possessive case (*his*).

> *The workers theirselves approved the new contract.
> REVISED: The workers themselves approved the new contract.

Here *selves* is added to the object case (*them*), not to the possessive case (*their*).

Name _____ Date _____

Exercise 1. Recognizing and Using Pronouns and Antecedents

Part A.   Each of the following includes one or more definite pronouns. Underline each one, number it, and identify its antecedent by
writing the corresponding number over it. If the antecedent is more
than one word, use brackets around it and put the number over the
first bracket. Circle any indefinite pronouns.

EXAMPLE

3 1, 2 1   2
[The president said <u>he</u> was delighted to be back in <u>his</u> own home-

     3
town.] That made (everyone) cheer.

1. Passengers who traveled on the S.S. *Perry* remember its spacious

  dining room and the way the captain always greeted them with

  a formal salute.

2. Gordon and Sheila are old friends; he has known her ever since

  she registered for lessons at his ski school in Utah.

3. Professor Helen Dorcas insists that her students should be able

  to write something about symbolism on their examinations.

4. The collapse of the first balcony has frightened many theater-

  goers; it indicates that the building may no longer be safe for

  anyone.

5. If no one reported hearing or seeing the plane that was scheduled to reach Fairbanks at noon, its pilot may have decided not to risk the lives of his passengers by taking them over the mountains in bad weather.

6. Betty told Frank she wanted him to bring a map so that they could choose the shortest route from the university to her family's home in Danville.

7. The movie stars Ronald Reagan as a cowboy whose companions survive many dangers because of his help.

8. The owners of Crampton's Market have decided to give a five-dollar rebate to customers whose purchases total fifty dollars or more. Whether this will attract new patrons to the market is unknown at present.

9. Somebody will have to tell the Smiths that their cat Fugee was eating a chocolate ice cream cone that he held in his front paws.

10. Harriet Glower has been named treasurer and assistant vice-president in charge of personnel. That will please everyone who knows her.

Name _____ Date _____

Exercise 1, *continued*

Part B. In each of the following, some pronouns have been omitted. Complete the sentences by writing in each blank a suitable pronoun that refers to one of the antecedents shown in italics.

EXAMPLE

Wanda invited all of __**her**__ teammates to her eighteenth-

birthday party.

1. *Frank* has sent a copy of _____ thesis to all of *the people*

   _____ joined forces to send _____ to college.

2. *Opera lovers* have been pleased to learn that _____ can now get

   recordings of arias sung by *Caruso,* _____ performances

   thrilled hundreds of thousands in Europe and the United States.

3. *The lawn* looked as if someone had used an eggbeater to mow

   _____ . _____ surface was very irregular.

4. Upon learning that *Wilbur* collected discarded matchbook covers,

   Ethel showed _____ to the door. _____ had had enough dates

   with young men like _____ .

5. *The new cafe* may not attract *people* _____ live in the neigh-

   borhood. Despite _____ excellent chef, _____ may not fre-

   quent the place, for _____ are slow to change _____ ways.

6. *A recommendation to shorten the term of the mayor to two*

   years is gaining support among *many voters.* _____ would

   give _____ more control over _____ town.

7. *James* is proud of *the new bumps on his head.* He insists that

   _____ are evidence of _____ growing intelligence.

8. *Ms. Little has kept* _____ *promise to cut the budget by 20 per-*

   cent. _____ should silence _____ critics for a spell.

9. *Firemen* are upset because _____ *costly new oxygen equipment*

   has not worked well. _____ has not helped _____ breathe when

   the temperature rises above 110 degrees.

10. An unexpected letter from *Susan* brightened *George's* day. _____

    always enjoyed hearing from _____ .

Name _____ Date _____

Exercise 2.   Recognizing and Using Clear and Correct Pronoun
Reference

Part A.   Each of the following consists of two sentences. One is correct; the other includes a pronoun that has no clear antecedent or that
does not agree with its antecedent in number. Circle the letter of the
correct sentence.

EXAMPLE

    a.   Judy said that they would take singing lessons.
   (b.) Judy said that she would take singing lessons.

1. a.   Donna and Frank finally ended his long-standing feud.
    b.   Donna and Frank finally ended their long-standing feud.

2. a.   The class groaned when it saw its grades.
    b.   The class groaned when they saw their grades.

3. a.   Before photographing the beetle, John examined it closely.
    b.   Before photographing the beetle, John examined them
        closely.

4. a.   Janet wrote immediately, but then forgot to mail it.
    b.   Janet wrote the letter immediately, but then forgot to mail
        it.

5. a.   Neither the owner nor the workers would change his po-
        sition.
    b.   Neither the owner nor the workers would change their po-
        sition.

6. a.   The sound of the bombs was so frightening that it drove
        everyone underground.
    b.   The sound of the bombs was so frightening that they drove
        everyone underground.

7. a.   Everyone had to wait for their turn.
    b.   Everyone had to wait for a turn.

8. a. Some of the boats had green stripes across their sides.
   b. Some of the boats had green stripes across its sides.

9. a. Many left their shoes in the hall.
   b. Many left his shoes in the hall.

10. a. When the light turns green, I can never seem to get away
    fast enough; they always start honking behind me before I
    start moving.
    b. When the light turns green, I can never seem to get away
    fast enough for the drivers behind me; they always start
    honking before I start moving.

Part B. In each of the following, underline each definite pronoun
except *I* and *me*. If the pronoun and its antecedent do not agree, circle
the pronoun, and write the correct form in the blank at right. If the
antecedent cannot be readily identified, circle the pronoun and write
a suitable replacement—a noun or noun phrase— in the blank at right.
If a sentence is correct as it stands, write *Correct.*

EXAMPLE

Each of the dogs stood up on (their) hind legs.   *its*

I saw a banjo clock and a statue of Mercury in the
antique store. I wanted to buy (it,) but I didn't
have the money.   *the clock*

1. Coffee beans must be picked by hand and then
   shipped long distances to processing plants. As a
   result, it can be expensive.   _____

2. The children and their grandfather like to stroll
   on the beach after having his lunch.   _____

3. With a pocketknife Uncle Frank carved a model
   of two seagulls and then gave them to me as a
   keepsake.   _____

4. During the wedding ceremony each of the ushers
   stood with their back to the congregation.   _____

154

Name _____ Date _____

Exercise 2, *continued*

5. Sally cooked most of the hamburgers at the pic-
   nic. It tasted great.   _____

6. When a baby cries, they may need help.   _____

7. Every homeowner should have their house fully
   insured.   _____

8. Sam and Fred both brought their cats.   _____

9. The company has announced that their new cars
   will be guaranteed against rust for five years.   _____

10. Neither the sergeant nor the men liked the orders
    they had been given.   _____

Name_____ Date_____

Exercise 3.   Recognizing and Using Correct Pronoun Case

Part A.   Each of the following consists of two sentences. In one sentence each pronoun is correct; in the other at least one pronoun is in the wrong case or is misspelled. Circle the letter of the sentence in which each pronoun is correct.

EXAMPLE

    a.   Fred gave some books to his brother and I.
    (b.)   Fred gave some books to his brother and me.

1. a.   The audience enthusiastically applauded him conducting.
   b.   The audience enthusiastically applauded his conducting.

2. a.   She and I seldom disagree.
   b.   Her and me seldom disagree.

3. a.   The evening talk show featured a judge whose reputation for toughness is well known.
   b.   The evening talk show featured a judge who's reputation for toughness is well known.

4. a.   The government has told factory owners that it is opposed to them investing in foreign enterprises.
   b.   The government has told factory owners that it is opposed to their investing in foreign enterprises.

5. a.   The mural was finished with the help of Mary and I.
   b.   The mural was finished with the help of Mary and me.

6. a.   The manager asked Howell and me to take inventory on Sunday.
   b.   The manager asked Howell and I to take inventory on Sunday.

7. a.   Peter cut hisself badly with the saw.
   b.   Peter cut himself badly with the saw.

8. a.   Slowly the expedition made it's way down the Amazon.
   b.   Slowly the expedition made its way down the Amazon.

9. a. Nancy Swallow is one government official on whom we can count for effective leadership.
   b. Nancy Swallow is one government official on who we can count for effective leadership.

10. a. The salesman offered Bradley and I a discount on the sofa, but we decided not to buy it.
    b. The salesman offered Bradley and me a discount on the sofa, but we decided not to buy it.

Part B. In each of the following sentences, circle any pronoun that is in the wrong case or is incorrectly spelled. Then write the correct form in the blank at right. If a sentence is correct as it stands, write *Correct*.

EXAMPLE

Philip returned (me) hat to me.   *my*

1. The budget director has informed Ethel Smith and I that we must reduce the costs of our department by 25 percent.   _____

2. When Frank Dazzle gave his concert, many in the audience resented him taking six intermissions in the first hour.   _____

3. Highway patrolmen have orders to stop motorists who's vehicles may not meet the state's safety standards.   _____

4. My cousin and me built the cabin without using any power tools.   _____

5. It was clear to the trainer and me that my days as a running back were over.   _____

6. After eight years of living under an assumed name, the terrorist turned hisself in.   _____

7. The president will confer with those officials from who he had no annual report.   _____

8. Because both parents have jobs, the children have to fend for theirself.   _____

9. The clock isn't running because it's main spring is broken.   _____

10. Professor Grant stunned the members of his calculus class by announcing that they would have fifty problems on they're final exam.   _____

158

10

SUBJECT-VERB
AGREEMENT

10.1   What Is Agreement?

To say that a verb **agrees** in form with its subject is to say that a verb
has more than one form, and that each form matches up with a particular kind of subject. Consider these examples:

> S
> The child / *has* a paper route.

> S
> The children / *have* a playground.

> S
> My sister / *is studying* chemistry.

> S
> I / *am studying* music.

> S
> We / *are attending* the same university.

> S
> The sky / *was* overcast.

> S
> The clouds / *were* thick.

To manage agreement correctly, you must know the rules of agreement; you must be able to identify each subject; and you must be able
to recognize the number of each subject—to tell whether it is singular
or plural.

10.2   Choosing the Verb Form—
Rules of Agreement   *sv agr*

Here are the rules governing agreement of subject and verb.

1. In most cases, the subject affects the form of the verb only when the verb is in the present tense. When the tense is present and the subject is a singular noun, add *-s* or *-es* to the bare form of the verb:

> The restaurant *specializes* in Greek dishes.
> Betty *runs* a printing press.
> Mickey *watches* television six hours a day.

Add *-s* or *-es* also when the subject is a third-person singular pronoun, such as *he, she, it, this,* or *everyone:*

> She *paints* houses.
> Everyone *wants* the latest news.
> The lemon *looks* juicy. It *tastes* sour.

Remember that the pronouns *you* and *I* are not in the third person.

2. When the tense is present and the subject is *not* a singular noun or a third-person singular pronoun, use the bare form of the verb:

> The owners *supervise* every transaction.
> They *do* their own bookkeeping.
> Gail and John *speak* four different languages.
> They *have* interesting jobs at the UN.
> They *live* in New York.

3. Whatever the subject, do not add *-s* or *-es* to a verb when it is used with an auxiliary, such as *does, can, may,* or *should:*

> *Does money *cures* all ills?
> REVISED: Does money *cure* all ills?

> *Doesn't she ever *sleeps?*
> REVISED: Doesn't she ever *sleep?*

> *Ellen can *dances* all night.
> REVISED: Ellen can *dance* all night.

> *Steve may *works* for the highway department next summer.
> REVISED: Steve may *work* for the highway department next summer.

> *Should the coach *decides* everything?
> REVISED: Should the coach *decide* everything?

4. Whatever the subject, do not add *-s* or *-es* to an infinitive—whether or not it is preceded by *to:*

> *Ruth allows her sister to *borrows* her clothes.
> REVISED: Ruth allows her sister to *borrow* her clothes. [infinitive with *to*]

> *Ruth lets her sister *borrows* her clothes.
> REVISED: Ruth lets her sister *borrow* her clothes. [infinitive without *to*]

5. Use the forms of *be* as shown here. This is the only verb in English with more than two forms in the present tense and more than one in the past:

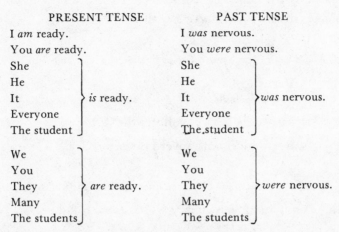

PRESENT TENSE	PAST TENSE
I *am* ready.	I *was* nervous.
You *are* ready.	You *were* nervous.
She He It > *is* ready. Everyone The student	She He It > *was* nervous. Everyone The student
We You They > *are* ready. Many The students	We You They > *were* nervous. Many The students

In speaking certain dialects of English, you may use such forms as *She be ready* and *They be ready*. But in writing Standard American English, you must use the forms shown here.

6. Use the forms shown here when *be* serves as an auxiliary:

> I *am* interested in computers.
> Each of the engines *is* checked once a day.
> Government workers *are* forbidden to strike.
> Sal *is* studying Chinese.
> Last year I *was* employed at the telephone company.
> Two of my friends *were* employed there too.
> Many people *were* hoping to see the castle.
> A sentry *was* guarding the entrance.

7. When the verb is *have,* whether by itself or as an auxiliary, use *has* if the subject is a singular noun or a third-person singular pronoun. With all other subjects, use the bare form, *have:*

> I *have* a complaint.
> Everyone *has* a complaint.
> Millions of people *have* seen the show.
> Jennifer *has* seen it too.
> Other shows *have* been highly praised.
> This one *has* been acclaimed.
> She *has been filing* tax forms for five hours.
> I *have been relaxing* since Friday.

10.3   Finding the Subject

Finding the subject is easy when it comes directly before the verb, as in the preceding examples. But you may have trouble finding subjects of certain kinds. These are listed next.

1. Subjects in sentences starting with *There* or *Here:*

$$S$$

There *were* / three motorcycles outside the restaurant.

$$S$$

Here *come* / the bulls.

In these sentences the subject follows the verb.

2. Subjects in sentences with inverted word order:

$$S$$

Underneath the pile of massive linemen *was* / the quarterback.

For this example, the customary word order would be:

$$S$$

The quarterback / *was* underneath the pile of massive linemen.

3. Subjects in some questions:

$$S$$

Has / a doctor / *examined* your eyes?

$$S$$

Where *do* / the miners / *sleep?*

4. Subjects followed by a linking verb and a predicate noun:

$$S$$

Juanita's favorite dish / *was* enchiladas.

$$S$$

Enchiladas / *were* Juanita's favorite dish.

The subject is the noun before the linking verb, not the one after it. Make the verb agree with the subject.

10.4 Recognizing the Number of the Subject

A subject is considered singular when it means one, and plural when it means two or more. Most subjects are made with words or word groups that are **fixed** in number; they are either singular or plural. But some subjects are made with words that are **variable** in number, changing with the contexts in which they are used.

10.5 Recognizing Number—Words and Word Groups Fixed in Number

Words and word groups fixed in number include most nouns and pronouns (whether modified or not), verbal nouns, and noun clauses.

Nouns

1. The number of most nouns is indicated by their spelling. A final *-s* or *-es* usually indicates the plural:

SINGULAR	PLURAL
car	cars
box	boxes
boss	bosses

Some nouns form the plural by changing their spelling in other ways:

SINGULAR	PLURAL
tooth	teeth
woman	women
child	children

2. A noun ending in *-s* but referring to just one thing is treated as singular:

> The news *was* shattering.
> Mumps *is* a painful disease.
> *Star Wars was* a spectacularly successful movie.
> *Giants in the Earth is* a powerful novel about settlers in the Dakota Territory.

3. Some nouns have no plural form:

> knowledge
> fortitude
> desperation

Pronouns

Some pronouns used as subjects are always treated as singular; some are always treated as plural:

ALWAYS SINGULAR

I	each	one
he	each one	another
she	everybody	somebody
it	everyone	someone
this	everything	something
that	either	whatever
anybody	neither	whichever
anyone	nobody	whoever
anything	none	
	no one	
	nothing	

ALWAYS PLURAL

we	these	both	others
they	those	few	several

Modified Nouns and Pronouns

The number of a modified noun or pronoun usually depends on the noun or pronoun itself—not on any of the modifiers attached to it. Normally, therefore, the verb should agree with the noun or pronoun—not with any of the modifiers.

> A man *was playing* a harmonica.
> A man surrounded by seven or eight children *was playing* a harmonica.
>
> Women *are encouraged* to apply.
> Women who want jobs *are encouraged* to apply.
>
> Each *has* a building permit.
> Each of the carpenters *has* a building permit.
>
> Neither *appeals* to many voters.
> Neither of the candidates *appeals* to many voters.
>
> Cartwright *supports* the new bill.
> Cartwright, along with many other senators, *supports* the new bill.
>
> Two salesclerks *were* on duty.
> Two salesclerks, together with the manager, *were* on duty.
>
> The child *has* a paper route.
> The child in the brown hat and rubber boots *has* a paper route.
>
> The clouds *were* thick.
> The clouds that hovered over Seattle *were* thick.

(Exceptions to this rule are discussed on p. 165.)

Verbal Nouns

A subject based on a verbal noun is treated as singular.

> To know her *is* to love her.

The simple subject is *to know,* a verbal noun.

> Reading maps *is* an inexpensive way to travel.

The simple subject is *Reading,* a verbal noun.

Noun Clauses

A subject consisting of a single noun clause is treated as singular:

> What Keynes said about public economy *is* still worth heeding.

10.6 Recognizing Number— Words Variable in Number

When the subject is made with a word that is variable in number, the number of the subject depends on the context in which the word is used—that is, on the words used with it. Several kinds of nouns and certain pronouns are variable in number. They are described next.

Nouns

1. A noun that is spelled the same in the plural as in the singular usually depends for its number on the words used with it:

> One small fish *was* all I caught.
> Three big fish *were* darting about near the water's edge.

In the first sentence *One* makes *fish* singular; in the second sentence *Three* makes the same word plural. Its form does not change.

> One popular series *features* Basil Whitheart as a judge.
> Three series *have been canceled* because of low ratings.

In the first sentence *One* makes *series* singular; in the second sentence *Three* makes the same word plural. Again, its form does not change. Other nouns of this type are *deer, sheep, moose, species,* and *means.*

2. A collective noun is singular when it refers to a unit, and plural when it refers to the individuals that make up the unit:

> The committee *meets* every Thursday night.
> The committee seldom *agree* on any issue involving money.

Other collective nouns are *audience, class, team, family,* and *crowd.*

3. A noun of whole measurement is singular when it means a unit, and plural when it refers to separate items:

> Fifty dollars *is* a lot to pay for a sun hat.
> Five quarts of pickles *were* left on the shelf.

Other nouns of whole measurement are *miles, pounds,* and *kilometers.*

4. A noun of partial measurement depends for its number on what is being measured:

> Half of the food *was* spoiled.
> Half of the students *were* absent.

Half of the food is singular because *food* is singular; *half of the students* is plural because *students* is plural.

5. The word *number* is plural when it follows *a,* and singular when it follows *the:*

> A number of customers *were* turned away.
> The number of places *is* limited.

Pronouns

Pronouns that are variable in number include *all, any, many, more, most, some, who, that,* and *which.* The number of such a pronoun depends on the number of the word or phrase to which it refers:

> Some of the snow *was melting.*

> Some of the snowflakes *were clinging* to the windowpane.

Students who *receive* financial aid are numerous.

A student who *receives* financial aid often has to work part time.

Many is singular when used with *a* or *an;* otherwise it is plural:

Many a hiker *has become* lost.

Many of the hikers *have become* lost.

10.7   Recognizing Number—Compound Subjects

1. When items joined by *and* or *both . . . and* refer to more than one person or thing, treat the subject as plural:

Both the author and the director *are* pleased with the show.

When items joined by *and* refer to one person or thing, treat the subject as singular:

The manager and shortstop *was* Leo Durocher.

2. When items are joined by *or, either . . . or, neither . . . nor, not . . . but,* or *not only . . . but also,* the verb should agree with the second item, no matter what the first is. Treat the subject as singular if the second item is singular, and as plural if the second item is plural:

Neither the two drummers nor the first violinist *was* at the rehearsal.
Not only the coach but also the players *dislike* the new turf.

Name _____ Date _____

Exercise 1. Recognizing Subject-Verb Agreement and Choosing Verb Forms

Part A. In each of the following sentences, underline the base verb. Then identify any infinitive (*INF*) and any auxiliary (*AUX*) that you find. If the sentence has an auxiliary, draw an arrow from that to the subject. Otherwise, draw an arrow from the base verb to the subject.

EXAMPLES

AUX
Does the skirt fit?

A nice cold drink tastes good on a hot day.

INF
Ruth lets her sister borrow her clothes.

1. Many men fix cars for a living.

2. Bob fixes bicycles.

3. I have three courses this term.

4. Karen has four.

5. The workers were angry.

6. The manager was stubborn.

7. The workers were expecting him to give them a raise.

8. At every class the teacher makes somebody give a speech.

9. My father gives a speech at the dinner table every night.

10. Does smoking cause cancer?

11. Many people hope to see taxes reduced.

12. A good discussion makes everyone see things in a new light.

13. How does an artist see the world?

14. An artist sees the world in a special way.

15. How do you see the world?

Part B. In each of the following sentences, one or more pairs of verb forms are given in parentheses. From each pair, choose the correct form, and write it in the blank at right.

EXAMPLE

Every day the coach (have, has) Jeff (do, does) thirty push-ups.

has, do

1. Most people (don't, doesn't) work on Sundays.

_____

2. But Father Francis (do, does).

_____

3. Money (are, is) the root of all evil.

_____

4. The train whistle (blow, blows) every night.

_____

5. Could a deaf person (hear, hears) it (blow, blows)?

_____

6. The engineer (make, makes) it (blow, blows).

_____

7. The bus (leave, leaves) at 4:05.

_____

8. Will it (reach, reaches) Indianapolis by six?

_____

9. Lemon juice (taste, tastes) bitter.

_____

10. Hogs (like, likes) mud.

_____

11. Connie (like, likes) bowling.

_____

12. Does she (like, likes) dancing?

_____

13. Fido (bark, barks) at all visitors.

_____

14. Some dogs (bark, barks) often.

_____

15. Any strange noise (make, makes) them (bark, barks).

_____

Name_____ Date_____

Exercise 2. Recognizing Subject Number

Each of the following sentences consists of one or more clauses. Circle each subject and draw an arrow from the subject to its verb or verb phrase. Then underline the verb or verb phrase once if the subject is singular and twice if it is plural.

EXAMPLE

(Kate and Harold) do not go to the movies any more because

(the price of tickets) has doubled in less than a year.

1. A mystery without a suspicious butler is like an omelet without an egg.

2. The cost of fuel oil has rarely decreased in recent years.

3. Few farmers in the region still have dairy herds.

4. Margaret Fuller is seeking reelection to the Board of Selectmen.

5. The pond has been declared a refuge for wildlife.

6. Many are planning to hear Philip Bryan, who has just returned from Moscow.

7. If everyone in the two groups contributes a dollar, the children will get new uniforms.

8. Nobody was sitting in the auditorium when part of the roof collapsed.

9. Some whales travel in large groups.

10. Although every member of the two orchestras is an experienced musician, none has ever played a composition by John Cage.

11. There is no evidence of bribery.

12. The old Sycamore Inn is now empty.

13. At the center of the bewildering maze of offices and narrow corridors is the computer.

14. Enforcing the laws against pollution of the seas is essential; without adequate enforcement, many skippers dump wastes as they please.

15. To find a fulfilling job is the hope of many who register for evening classes at the business school.

16. There are no paved roads in the bush.

17. One initial result of mass production was lower unit costs.

18. The citizens of Plotz are proud of their resistance to tyranny.

19. The news of Dan Mark's resignation has been greeted with no little skepticism by correspondents who know him.

20. A calendar with pictures of colorful birds hangs from a nail near the kitchen door.

Name _____ Date _____

Exercise 3.   Recognizing Subject Number and Choosing Verb Forms

In each of the following sentences, underline each subject once if it is singular and twice if it is plural. Then wherever a pair of verb forms is given in parentheses, choose the correct form, and circle it.

EXAMPLE

Betty always (smile, smiles) when the Cowboys (win, wins).

1. Everyone (carry, carries) an umbrella because the days (are, is) usually rainy.

2. Fred and Bob (are planning, is planning) to open a bakery as soon as the bank (give, gives) them a loan.

3. There (are, is) two ways in which an inexperienced observer (go, goes) wrong.

4. The rooms (have, has) been chilly ever since the thermostat (were, was) set at 55 degrees.

5. The Smith sisters (are, is) fond of the valley; neither (want, wants) to live anywhere else.

6. Repairing old clocks (were, was) originally a hobby; now it (are, is) a business.

7. Sally and Ethel (do, does) not find all modern novelists boring; both (have, has) two or three favorites whose latest book they (read, reads) as soon as it (are, is) published.

8. Behind a thick mass of dense underbrush and fallen trees (stand, stands) a sundial.

9. *The Grapes of Wrath,* by John Steinbeck, (tell, tells) about the Joads, who (travel, travels) to California during the Great Depression.

10. Whenever Alex (do, does) his imitation of Donald Duck, somebody (get, gets) a stitch from laughing.

11. The Grants, together with Peter Sprigg, (are, is) building an apartment house with solar heating.

12. Most of the old bricks (crumble, crumbles) under pressure.

13. A number of injured birds (are, is) found at the foot of the tower almost every morning.

14. The most valuable cargo in the ship's history (were, was) fifty thousand gold ingots.

15. Many a pilot (have, has) feared to cross Devil's Channel in stormy seas.

16. Most of the paintings (were, was) destroyed by the fire.

17. Not only Alaska but also Canada (have, has) spectacular mountains.

18. Each of the sentries (realize, realizes) that the others in the company (depend, depends) on him for protection.

19. In times of inflation $80,000 (are, is) not an unusual price for a small house.

20. During the graduation ceremonies, the class (cheer, cheers) the prizewinners and (sing, sings) a few songs.

Name_____ Date_____

Exercise 4.   Correcting Verb Forms

In each of the following sentences, circle any verb or verb phrase that does not agree with its subject. Then write the correct form in the blank at right. If a sentence is correct as it stands, write *Correct*.

EXAMPLES

She (watch) the sun rise every morning.   *watches*

One of the boards (have been taken.)   *has been taken.*

1. Whenever our dog wants attention, he

   start barking.   _____

2. Both of the secretaries have important

   jobs in the organization; each make a

   necessary contribution.   _____

3. There are a large pile of oyster shells

   in the middle of the lawn.   _____

4. To develop new skills are a gratifying

   experience for many.   _____

5. Salads with no dressing tastes strange;

   so does spareribs without a sauce.   _____

6. Discovering the legendary Northwest

   Passage to the Indies were the dream

   of many explorers.   _____

7. News of the surrender were signaled by the ringing of church bells.   _____

8. The city has been quiet for two nights because everyone now agrees that the rioting have accomplished nothing.   _____

9. A transport plane with space for two hundred infantrymen and all their equipment is scheduled for production in 1985.   _____

10. On the highest point of the twelve spires there is a golden cross.   _____

11. Jackson, along with two colonels, were mistaken for the enemy.   _____

12. The number of shootings in the neighborhood have increased since the election.   _____

13. Neither Jonathan nor his two partners has any doubts about the legitimacy of my complaint.   _____

14. Neither of the two applicants was fully qualified for the position.   _____

15. Asking us to pay a fee of a hundred dollars take a lot of nerve.   _____

16. Many an attorney have tried to become wealthy at our expense.   _____

Name _____ Date _____

Exercise 4, *continued*

17. Part of the document looks authentic,
    but scholars doubt whether all of it
    was written before A.D. 75.   _____

18. The chef's specialty are flaming peach-
    es set in vanilla ice cream.   _____

19. An outbreak of measles are no laugh-
    ing matter.   _____

20. A juggler, as well as several musicians,
    were entertaining visitors to the fair. _____

11

VERBS
Tense

11.1 Tense and Time

The **tense** of a verb helps to indicate the time of an action or condition:

> PAST: I *spent* last weekend raking leaves.
> PRESENT: As I *write* these words, more leaves *are falling*.
> FUTURE: I *will rake* those leaves next weekend.

But tense is not the same as time. A verb in the present tense, for instance, may be used in a statement about the future:

> Football practice *starts* next Wednesday.

As in this example, the time of an action or state is often indicated by a word or phrase like *yesterday, next Wednesday,* or *in 1865.*

11.2 Forming the Tenses *tf*

Forming the Principal Parts of Verbs

The tenses of all but a few verbs are made from the four **principal parts**: the present (also called the "bare" form), the present participle, the past, and the past participle. The principal parts of most verbs are formed by the addition of certain endings to the bare form: *-ing* for the present participle, and *-d* or *-ed* for the past and the past participle. Verbs with principal parts formed in this way are called **regular**.

PRESENT (BARE FORM)	PRESENT PARTICIPLE	PAST	PAST PARTICIPLE
walk	walk*ing*	walk*ed*	walk*ed*
sand	sand*ing*	sand*ed*	sand*ed*
move	mov*ing*	mov*ed*	mov*ed*

177

(As the last of these examples shows, a final *e* drops out when *-ing* is added.)

Verbs with some principal parts formed in special ways are called **irregular.** Here are some examples:

PRESENT (BARE FORM)	PRESENT PARTICIPLE	PAST	PAST PARTICIPLE
break	breaking	broke	broken
draw	drawing	drew	drawn
ride	riding	rode	ridden
steal	stealing	stole	stolen
sweep	sweeping	swept	swept
teach	teaching	taught	taught

(For the principal parts of commonly used irregular verbs, see section 11.5, p. 183.)

Forming the Present

With most subjects, the form of a verb in the present tense is simply the bare form:

Journalists *live* a hard life; they *rush* to meet deadlines.

But when the subject is a singular noun or a third-person singular pronoun, such as *he, it, that,* or *someone,* you must add *-s* or *-es* to the bare form of the verb:

Nicole *lives* far from town.
Every weekday she *rushes* to the office.

(For more on this point, see section 10.2, pp. 159–61.)

Forming the Past

The past tense of regular verbs is formed by the addition of *-d* or *-ed* to the bare form:

Nicole *lived* far from town.
She *rushed* to the office.

(For the past tense of commonly used irregular verbs, see section 11.5, p. 183.)

Forming Tenses with Auxiliaries

Besides the present and the past, there are four other tenses. You form these by using auxiliary verbs, such as *will, have,* and *had:*

	REGULAR VERB	IRREGULAR VERB
FUTURE:	They will race.	She will teach.
PRESENT PERFECT:	They have raced.	She has taught.
PAST PERFECT:	They had raced.	She had taught.
FUTURE PERFECT:	They will have raced.	She will have taught.

Using Common and Progressive Forms

For most verbs, each tense can be written in two ways. The **common** forms discussed so far indicate a momentary, habitual, or completed action. The **progressive** forms indicate that the action named by the verb phrase is viewed as continuing.

TENSE	COMMON FORM	PROGRESSIVE FORM
PRESENT	She works.	She is working.
PAST	She sang.	She was singing.
FUTURE	We will talk.	We will be talking.
PRESENT PERFECT	It has rained.	It has been raining.
PAST PERFECT	They had called.	They had been calling.
FUTURE PERFECT	You will have written.	You will have been writing.

As these examples show, the progressive form consists of the auxiliary *be* in some form, such as *is, was, will be,* or *have been,* followed by the present participle—the form with *-ing*—of the base verb.

Using *have, be,* and *do*

Three auxiliaries have major roles in forming tenses. As we have seen, *have* is used in forming the perfect tenses, and *be* in forming the progressive. The third auxiliary is *do,* used in forming some negatives, some questions, and emphatic statements:

> I do not smoke.
> Do you smoke?
> No, but I do take a drink now and then.

Have, be, and *do* are used to form tenses as follows:

1. *Have*

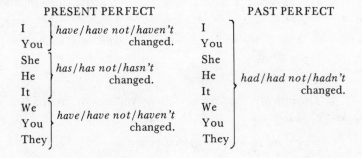

2. *Be*

	PRESENT PROGRESSIVE	PAST PROGRESSIVE
	I *am/am not* resting.	I *was/was not/wasn't* resting.
	You *are/are not/aren't* resting.	You *were/were not/weren't* resting.
She / He / It	*is/is not/isn't* resting.	*was/was not/wasn't* resting.
We / You / They	*are/are not/aren't* resting.	*were/were not/weren't* resting.

3. *Do*

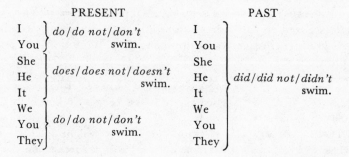

	PRESENT		PAST

I
You } *do/do not/don't* swim.

She
He } *does/does not/doesn't* swim.
It

We
You } *do/do not/don't* swim.
They

I
You
She
He } *did/did not/didn't* swim.
It
We
You
They

11.3   Using the Tenses   *tu*

The Present

1. Use the *common present*—

   1. To report what a person or thing does regularly:

     Michael *checks* the temperature every morning.

   2. To state a fact or a widely held belief:

     Hot air *rises.*
     In the opinion of many, some dreams *foretell* our future.

   3. To describe characters, events, or other matters in an aesthetic work, such as a painting, a piece of music, a work of literature, a movie, or a television show:

     In the third act the mother *recognizes* her long-absent son.

   4. To say what a writer or a creative artist does in his or her work:

     In *Walden*, Henry David Thoreau *describes* what he considers a good life.

2. Use the *present progressive*—

   1. To indicate that an action or state is occurring at the time of the writing:

     People *are yelling* in the street below my window.

   2. To indicate that an action is in progress—even though it may not be taking place at the exact moment of the writing:

     Workmen *are widening* the entrance to the harbor.

The Present Perfect

1. Use the *common present perfect*—

   1. To report a past action or state that touches in some way on the present:

     I *have* just *discussed* my academic record with the dean of freshmen.

2. To report an action or state begun in the past but extending into the present:

> The well *has been* dry since last August.

2. Use the *progressive* form of the *present perfect* to emphasize the continuity of an action that began in the past and is still occurring:

> Lawyers *have been wrangling* about the case for months.

The Past

1. Use the *common past*—

 1. To report an action or state definitely completed in the past:

 > Fenwick *bobbled* a fly ball in yesterday's game.

 2. To report an action repeated in the past but no longer occurring at the time of the writing:

 > They *ate* fish every Wednesday.

2. Use the *past progressive*—

 1. To emphasize the continuity of a past action:

 > The children *were making* castles in the wet sand.

 2. To say that one action was being performed when another occurred:

 > Fred *was tossing* cartons in the air when the supervisor appeared.

The Past Perfect

1. Use the *common past perfect*—

 1. To say that an action or state was completed by a specified time in the past:

 > By Friday noon the fog *had lifted.*

 2. To indicate that one past action or state was completed by the time another past action or state occurred:

 > Meg lost her way although she *had driven* to the house once before.

2. Use the *progressive* form of the *past perfect* to say that the first of two past actions went on until the second occurred:

> Carpenters *had been using* pine boards for roofing until someone demonstrated the advantages of plywood.

The Future

1. Use the *common future*—

 1. To report a future event or state that will definitely occur:

 > The moon *will enter* the second quarter next Wednesday.

2. To indicate willingness or determination to do something:

> We *will help* you on Saturday.

3. To report what will happen under certain conditions:

> If you eat tainted meat, you *will be* sick.

2. Use the *future progressive*—

1. To say that an action will be continuing for a period of time in the future:

> The committee *will be counting* votes all night.

2. To say what someone or something will be doing at a given time in the future:

> Our flag *will be flying* on July 4.

The Future Perfect

1. Use the *common future perfect*—

1. To say that an action or state will be completed by a specified time in the future:

> The enemy *will have attacked* by noon.

2. To say that an action or state will be completed by the time something else happens:

> The enemy *will have attacked* by the time reinforcements reach the fort.

2. Use the *progressive* form of the *future perfect* to say that an activity or state will continue until a specified time in the future:

> By six tonight the contestants *will have been dancing* for ten hours.

11.4   Tense and Time with Participles and Infinitives

Participles and infinitives have two tenses: the present and the perfect. The present consists of the present participle or the infinitive by itself. The perfect participle consists of *having* and the past participle; the perfect infinitive requires *have* between *to* and the past participle.

1. Use the present tense when the action or state named by the participle or infinitive occurs at or after the time of the main verb:

> *Sensing* danger, the beaver sounds a warning.
> *Sensing* danger, the beaver sounded a warning.

> He wants *to finish* the experiment.
> He wanted *to finish* the experiment.

2. Use the perfect tense when the action or state named by the participle or infinitive occurred before the time of the main verb:

> *Having spent* all my money, I had to walk home.
> We were sorry *to have missed* the party.

11.5 Principal Parts of Commonly Used Irregular Verbs

PRESENT (BARE FORM)	PRESENT PARTICIPLE	PAST	PAST PARTICIPLE
be†	being	was	been
begin	beginning	began	begun
bite	biting	bit	bitten
blow	blowing	blew	blown
break	breaking	broke	broken
bring	bringing	brought	brought
build	building	built	built
buy	buying	bought	bought
catch	catching	caught	caught
choose	choosing	chose	chosen
come	coming	came	come
dig	digging	dug	dug
do	doing	did	done
draw	drawing	drew	drawn
drink	drinking	drank	drunk, drunken
drive	driving	drove	driven
eat	eating	ate	eaten
fall	falling	fell	fallen
feel	feeling	felt	felt
fight	fighting	fought	fought
find	finding	found	found
fly	flying	flew	flown
give	giving	gave	given
go	going	went	gone
grow	growing	grew	grown
have	having	had	had
hold	holding	held	held
keep	keeping	kept	kept
know	knowing	knew	known
lay [put down]	laying	laid	laid
lead	leading	led	led
leave	leaving	left	left
lie [recline]	lying	lay	lain
make	making	made	made
ride	riding	rode	ridden
rise	rising	rose	risen
run	running	ran	run
see	seeing	saw	seen
shake	shaking	shook	shaken
shine	shining	shone	shone
sing	singing	sang	sung
speak	speaking	spoke	spoken
spring	springing	sprang	sprung
swear	swearing	swore	sworn
swim	swimming	swam	swum
throw	throwing	threw	thrown
wear	wearing	wore	worn

†In this one case the bare form *(be)* is not the same as the present *(am, is, are)*.

Name_____ Date_____

Exercise 1. Choosing Verb Forms and Writing Principal Parts

In each of the following sentences, choose from the pair of verb forms in parentheses the one that is correct in the sentence, and circle it. Then identify the verb as regular (*R*) or irregular (*I*), and write out the four principal parts: the present (bare form), the present participle, the past, and the past participle. Consult the list of irregular verbs in section 11.5 (p. 183) if necessary.

EXAMPLES

Last year she (give, (gave)) a party for three hundred people.

(I) give giving gave given

On his third try Jack (pass, (passed)) the test.

(R) pass passing passed passed

1. Mayor Mitchell (leaded, led) the parade.

2. Yesterday I (walk, walked) home.

3. By early December all the leaves had (fell, fallen).

4. The birds had (flewed, flown) south.

5. Running through the brambles last night, I (scratch, scratched) my leg.

6. Winter (began, beginned) with a huge snowfall on Thanksgiving Day.

7. At the supermarket we (buyed, bought) two dozen eggs.

8. After the wax job the old car (shined, shone) like a mirror.

9. Last week the little boys (sneer, sneered) at the old man.

10. After the fight he (sweared, swore) to get even.

11. The angry dog (bit, bited) the child on the leg.

12. The pitcher (throwed, threw) two curve balls in a row.

13. In the first grade I (learn, learned) nothing but the alphabet.

14. The old man (shaked, shook) his fist at me.

15. Around her neck she (weared, wore) a yellow ribbon.

16. At 7:00 A.M. the trumpeter (blowed, blew) reveille.

17. The cat (springed, sprang) from the table.

Name _____ Date _____

Exercise 1, *continued*

18. During the whole evening she had (smiled, smile) just once.

19. I (keeped, kept) the picture for years.

20. Then we all (singed, sang) "Home on the Range."

21. Every day she (swimmed, swam) twenty laps.

22. By the end of the week we had (ate, eaten) all our food.

23. My brother has (sawed, seen) *Star Wars* six times.

24. A big crowd (comed, came) to see the ceremony.

25. On the blackboard someone had (drawed, drawn) a swastika.

Name_____ Date_____

Exercise 2. Using Tenses

Each of the following consists of two sentences, one complete and one with a verb omitted but the bare form given in parentheses. Complete the second sentence by writing in the blank the correct form of the parenthesized verb, using the tense of the italicized verb in the first sentence.

EXAMPLE

In the last scene of the movie, the hero *captures* the villains.

In the last scene of the play, the heroine __*denounces*__ her

cruel uncle. (denounce)

1. The girls *have been chanting* slogans for the last thirty minutes.

    The porpoises_____jumps for fifteen

    minutes. (practice)

2. Most of the birds *will migrate* in the autumn.

    The ice in the ponds_____ in the spring. (thaw)

3. Americans *honor* their founding fathers on July 4.

    The French_____the beginning of their revolution

    on Bastille Day. (commemorate)

4. We *had been working* for at least two hours when the alarm

    sounded.

    When the concert finally began, the audience_____

    _____ for almost an hour. (wait)

5. She *has* just *seen* a performance of *Hamlet;* she can't get the last scene out of her mind.

We_____ just_____ a recording of Pavarotti; he certainly has a splendid voice. (hear)

6. Daily exercise *promotes* good health.

Regular maintenance _____ the life of a car. (prolong)

7. We *were writing* our examinations when the lights went out.

I _____ a shower when the phone rang. (take)

8. Sharon *won* the lawsuit.

Then she _____ a big fee. (collect)

9. By the time I reached the store, someone else *had* already *bought* the camera.

By the end of the second week I _____ all my money. (spend)

10. The big platter slipped out of my hands and *fell* to the floor.

It _____ into little pieces. (break)

12

VERBS
Sequence of Tenses

When a passage has more than one verb, the relation between the tenses of the verbs is called the **sequence of tenses.** Various sequences are possible.

12.1 Sequence of Tenses in a Sentence

When all of the verbs in a sentence describe actions or states that occur at or about the same time, their tenses should be the same:

> As the plane *lifted* from the runway, I *settled* back in my seat. [both past tense]
> When the ground *begins* to thaw, the dirt roads *become* mud bogs. [both present tense]

But of course actions do not always happen at the same time, even if they are described in the same sentence. A sentence may report actions and conditions that occur at different times, and it will then have verbs in different tenses. In other words, the tense in the sentence will shift. The nature of the shift will depend on the kind of clauses in which the verbs appear.

When the clauses are **independent,** the tenses of the verbs in those clauses may be independent of each other:

> I *jogged* every day during the summer, so now I *feel* healthy. [past and present]
> I *am taking* physics this term; next term I *will take* chemistry. [present and future]

When one or more of the clauses are **subordinate,** the tense of the subordinate verb depends on the tense of the main verb, as shown in the examples that follow.

Main Verb in the Present

When the main verb is in the present tense, the subordinate verb is commonly in the present also:

MAIN VERB	SUBORDINATE VERB
The trains *leave* the station	as soon as the computer *gives* the signal.

The subordinate verb is in the present perfect or the past only when it refers to action that occurred before the time of the main verb:

MAIN VERB	SUBORDINATE VERB
	PRESENT PERFECT
Most of the soldiers *are* sent overseas	when they *have completed* their basic training.
	PAST
The Careys *love* the house,	which they *restored* with their own hands.

The subordinate verb is in the future when it refers to action in the future:

MAIN VERB	SUBORDINATE VERB
	FUTURE
During the fall worshipers *prepare* gifts	that they *will offer* to the Christ child at Christmas.

Main Verb in the Past

When the main verb is in the past tense, the subordinate verb is normally in the past or past perfect tense. An auxiliary verb in the subordinate clause should also be in the past tense, taking a form like *was, were, had, did, could, might, should, used to,* or *would:*

MAIN VERB	SUBORDINATE VERB
	PAST
The legislators *postponed* a vote on the bill	because they *wanted* more time to evaluate its probable impact on the economy.
	PAST PERFECT
The astronaut *showed* us three rocks	that he *had taken* from the moon.
	PAST
Before the meeting few employees *believed*	that the manager *would resign.*

12.2 Sequence of Tenses in a Paragraph

A single sentence can often include more than one verb and more than one tense. A paragraph normally includes many verbs and often several different tenses. But you should shift tenses in a paragraph only when you have good reason for doing so.

A well-written paragraph is normally dominated by just one tense. Consider the following paragraph:

> This is more protection than the mountain lion, bobcat or fox gets in our state. All these predators must be considered rare in the Southwest and possibly in danger of extinction. All but the mountain lion are regarded as varmints, without protection. Although the mountain lion was recently given big-game status in Arizona, it may still be trapped or hunted at any time by any rancher who claims he is losing livestock to lions. On this basis alone twenty-four lions were trapped and killed in one county in Arizona in 1972. At that rate of loss, the lion will not last long as a species.
>
> —Edward Abbey, "The Great Globe Arizona Wild Pig and Varmint Hunt"

The author is describing a present condition in the state of Arizona, so the dominant tense here is the present. That is the tense, for example, of *is, gets, must be considered, are regarded*. But there are two shifts from the present. To describe what has already happened to mountain lions, he shifts to the past tense in the fourth and fifth sentences: *was given, were trapped and killed*. Then, to say what will happen to the lion, he shifts to the future tense in the last sentence: *will not last*. So he clearly has a good reason for each shift in tense.

12.3 Faulty Tense Shifts *shift*

As the preceding examples show, a single sentence can often include verbs with different tenses. The shift of tenses is faulty, however, when the tense of one verb does not correspond properly to the tense of another. Consider this example:

> *The mural *depicts* pioneers who *are clearing* woodland for farms, townspeople who *are building* schools and churches, legislators who *are debating* in the new capitol, and young adventurers who *were journeying* westward.

The shift from the present tense to the past (*were journeying*) is faulty. Since the time of all the actions is the same, the tense of all the verbs reporting them should be the same:

> The mural *depicts* pioneers who *are clearing* woodland for farms, townspeople who *are building* schools and churches, legislators who *are debating* in the new capitol, and young adventurers who *are journeying* westward.

Here is another example:

> *Washington *told* his soldiers to open fire when the Redcoats *attack*.

The shift to the present (*attack*) is faulty. When the main verb is in the past, the subordinate verb must be in the past or past perfect:

> Washington *told* his soldiers to open fire when the Redcoats *attacked*.

Here is one more example:

> *Harry *wants* to show his friends the photographs he *had taken* during his recent trip to Mexico.

A main verb in the present (*wants*) should not be followed by a subordinate verb in the past perfect. In this sentence the subordinate verb should be in the past:

> Harry *wants* to show his friends the photographs he *took* during his recent trip to Mexico.

And here is a final example:

> *Everyone *hopes* that the plan *would work*.

The main verb in the present (*hopes*) should in this instance be followed by a subordinate verb in the future:

> Everyone *hopes* that the plan *will work*.

Use *would* in a sentence like this only if the main verb is in the past:

> Everyone *hoped* that the plan *would work*.

Name_____ Date_____

Exercise 1.   Recognizing Verbs and Choosing Tenses

Part A.   In each of the following sentences, underline the verbs.

EXAMPLES

Brenda <u>cheered</u> when she <u>heard</u> the news.

Cal <u>has seen</u> every movie that Bogart ever <u>made</u>.

1. Bernard and Elsa will be married after they find a house north of Boston.

2. For years fishermen tried to protect themselves from blackflies by coating the exposed parts of their bodies with foul-smelling pastes they had heard about from fishermen before them.

3. Insects probe the stoutest defenses until they find a way to their target.

4. Though some insect repellents have been produced by learned chemists, no one feels safe outdoors on warm summer evenings.

5. Many children and adults perished in the great wave of influenza that raged across the United States in 1918.

6. The drawing represents a player in uniform who is holding a football against his chest and leaning to the left as if to avoid a tackler.

7. Proud of his carpentry, the old-timer told his sons he would finish the roofing by himself.

8. While not all last-minute Christmas shoppers are violent, many disregard the rights of others in their push to get what they want.

9. My grandfather did not have an easy childhood, and he never earned a high school diploma; but he was a success in many ways.

10. To save money on fuel, a neighbor is installing solar panels in the roof of his house; but I wonder what will happen if we have a stretch of cloudy weather.

Part B. In each of the following sentences, choose from the verb forms in parentheses the one that corresponds properly in tense to the italicized verb. Then write the form you have chosen in the blank at right.

EXAMPLE

As soon as the audience *was* quiet, the con-   *raised*
ductor (raises, raised) his baton.

1. Scientists *seek* to verify a hypothesis through a   _____
series of experiments that they (conduct, con-
ducted) under laboratory conditions.

2. Whenever the interest rate on loans *is lowered,*   _____
the number of applicants for mortgages (increases,
increased).

3. The manager *is encouraged* by the way the sales-   _____
clerks (have worked, worked, work) since the new
labor contract (was negotiated, is negotiated) last   _____
month.

4. The hunter *spotted* a lion shortly before sun-   _____
down; then he (lost, loses) sight of it in the bush.

5. At the start of the story the young heroine *is*   _____
looking for work in the television industry, so
she (made, makes) the round of major studios.

6. Dogs *are allowed* on the premises provided they   _____
(are kept, were kept) on a leash.

Name _____ Date _____

Exercise 1, *continued*

7. On June 1 the employees at Plant 3 *went* on   _____
    strike because no settlement of their grievances
    (is reached, had been reached).

8. The children *are smiling* because the principal   _____
    (had announced, has announced) a holiday.

9. In the past hikers *carried* some type of garment   _____
    which (protects, protected) them from inclement
    weather.

10. Though some runners never *work out* the day   _____
    before a race, many (did, do).

Name_____ Date _____

Exercise 2.   Correcting Faulty Tense Shifts

In each of the following sentences, circle any verb that does not correspond properly in tense to the italicized verb. Then write the correct form in the blank at right. If a sentence is correct as it stands, write *Correct*.

EXAMPLE

The wailing of sirens *announced* the arrival of the motorcade; moments later, the president's limousine (comes) into view.   *came*

1. Precautions *are being taken* to prevent an outbreak of the fighting that had marred the fair a year ago.   _____

2. Diplomas *were granted* to students who complete all of their courses.   _____

3. Fishermen in the small town *are troubled* because the average size of their catch had diminished steadily since 1977.   _____

4. During the summer carpenters *repaired* the damage that an ice storm causes during the previous winter.   _____

5. When speaking with civic officials, my aunt always *finds* a way to remind them that they are servants of the public.   _____

6. It *is* strange how whispering, not talking, can trouble others who were trying to concentrate.   _____

7. The chance of rain *was* so slight that no one brings an umbrella. _____

8. Before fertilizer was added, the soil *is prepared* with watering and raking. _____

9. Some people who saw the strange lights *thought* that a UFO is hovering over the pasture. _____

10. Lightning *struck* the house just after it is rebuilt. _____

Name_____ Date _____

Exercise 3. Changing Tense Forms

In each of the following sentences, make the tense of the italicized verb past if it is present, and present if it is past. Then rewrite the sentence, changing the tense of every other verb as necessary to make the sequence of tenses correct.

EXAMPLE

The two children *played* in the sandbox until recess ended.

> play
> The two children play in the sandbox until recess ends.

1. Bert *claims* that he has never been late for work.

2. One company in the area *is working* to develop a type of insulation that will reduce the loss of heat through windows.

3. The children *had* trails going in every conceivable direction, but the favorite was one that went straight downhill and under the barbed-wire fence.

4. Whenever Nick drives, Melanie *sits* in the back seat with her feet braced against the front seat.

5. The fugitive *knew* that wherever he went, someone would be on the lookout, eager to collect the reward.

6. Printed on the back *are* directions that explain how the kit is to be assembled.

7. We *were* lucky that the epidemic hadn't taken all of us.

8. As the years go by, my father *adds* new vegetables to a garden he first planted in 1970.

9. Chet *did* his own long-distance driving, while Herb managed the short trips and Helen ran the office.

10. Though the waiters have certain traits in common, each *has* his own mannerisms that please some customers and annoy others.

13

VERBS
Active and
Passive Voice

The word "voice" generally refers to the sound of someone speaking. But as applied to sentences, "voice" has to do with verbs. When the subject of a verb acts, the verb is in the **active voice**; when the subject is acted upon, the verb is in the **passive voice**:

> ACTIVE: The crowd *cheered* the speaker.
> PASSIVE: The speaker *was cheered* by the crowd.

13.1   Changing from Active to Passive

An active-voice verb that has a direct object can be changed to the passive voice:

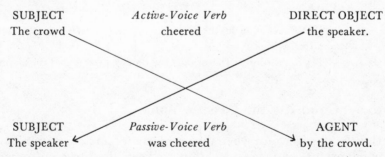

SUBJECT	*Active-Voice Verb*	DIRECT OBJECT
The crowd	cheered	the speaker.

SUBJECT	*Passive-Voice Verb*	AGENT
The speaker	was cheered	by the crowd.

The direct object of the active-voice verb becomes the subject of the passive-voice verb, and the subject of the active-voice verb becomes the **agent** of the passive-voice verb—the one by whom the action is said to be performed. The word *by* goes before the agent.

You can drop the agent if the performer of an action is unimportant or clearly implied in the sentence with the passive-voice verb:

> The speaker was repeatedly heckled.
> Salmon are found in the colder regions of the Northern Hemisphere.

13.2 Changing from Passive to Active

A passive-voice verb that is followed by a phrase specifying an agent can be changed to the active voice:

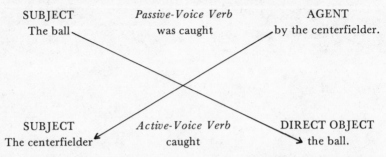

SUBJECT   *Passive-Voice Verb*   AGENT
The ball   was caught   by the centerfielder.

SUBJECT   *Active-Voice Verb*   DIRECT OBJECT
The centerfielder   caught   the ball.

The subject of the passive-voice verb becomes the direct object of the active-voice verb. The agent of the passive-voice verb—the one by whom the action is performed—becomes the subject of the active-voice verb. The word *by* drops out.

Normally you can change a verb from passive to active only if it is followed by a *by* phrase naming an agent. If no agent is named, you must either keep the passive voice or supply the agent before changing to the active voice:

> New Orleans was founded about 1718.
> New Orleans was founded about 1718 by Jean Baptiste Lemoyne.
> Jean Baptiste Lemoyne founded New Orleans about 1718.

13.3 Choosing the Active Voice

Use the active voice to make your writing vigorous, direct, and concise. Compare:

> PASSIVE: As soon as the flames *were seen* by Dalton, the alarm *was sounded* by him.
> ACTIVE: As soon as Dalton *saw* the flames, he *sounded* the alarm.

13.4 Choosing the Passive Voice

Use the passive voice when the performer of an action is unknown or unimportant, or when you want to keep the focus on someone or something important that is acted upon:

> Every year, tons of litter *are thrown* along our nation's highways.
> On November 22, 1963, John F. Kennedy *was assassinated* in Dallas, Texas.

13.5   Misusing the Passive Voice   *pass*

Changing from Active to Passive without Good Reason

Do not switch from active to passive voice in midsentence without a good reason:

> The car *skidded, bounced* over the curb, and then a tree *was struck.*

Since the subject of this sentence performed all of the actions described, the writer has no good reason to switch from the active voice of *skidded* and *bounced* to the passive voice of *was struck.* The voice of all the verbs should be active:

> The car *skidded, bounced* over the curb, and then *struck* a tree.

Overusing the Passive

Do not overuse the passive voice. Overuse of the passive drains the life out of writing and often leaves the reader wondering who or what is performing the actions described:

> After ten dollars *was won* at Chuck-a-Luck, a ride on the roller coaster *was taken.*

The writer of this sentence presumably knows who won the money and rode the roller coaster. The writer should therefore tell us, and should make this person the subject of active verbs:

> After she won ten dollars at Chuck-a-Luck, Jan took a ride on the roller coaster.

Name_____ Date_____

Exercise 1. Recognizing and Transforming Voice

In each of the following sentences, underline the verb, and identify the voice of the verb as active (*A*) or passive (*P*). Then rewrite the sentence, changing the voice.

EXAMPLES

The fiery speaker <ins>was cheered</ins> by the crowd. **P**

The crowd cheered the fiery speaker.

Huge floodlights <ins>illuminated</ins> the ballfield. **A**

The ballfield was illuminated by huge floodlights.

1. In 1793 the French city of Toulon was occupied by British troops.

2. In the French attack on the British troops, Napoleon commanded the artillery forces.

3. The British were routed by the French.

4. In 1796 Napoleon defeated the Sardinians.

5. In the same year Milan was captured by Napoleon.

6. After Napoleon's capture of Moscow in 1812, the Russian winter severely weakened his army.

7. At the Battle of Leipzig in 1813, Napoleon was beaten by a coalition of European armies.

8. He was driven into France by these armies.

9. On March 30, 1814, these armies attacked Napoleon on three sides.

10. On April 11, 1814, the allies exiled him to the island of Elba.

Name_____ Date_____

Exercise 2.   Correcting Misuses of the Passive Voice

Revise any of the following sentences in which the passive voice is used where the active voice would be more effective. If you think the passive voice is effectively used, write *Effective*.

EXAMPLE

The car skidded, bounced over the curb, and then a tree was struck.

The car skidded, bounced over the curb, and then struck a tree.

1. Since I last saw the dentist, my teeth have been carefully brushed twice a day.

2. During our stay in Arizona, the Grand Canyon was seen.

3. As he walked down the stairs, a pain in his hip was felt.

4. Rowaleski made a spectacular run, but he was tackled on the fifteen-yard line.

5. Since I needed exercise, a long run was taken.

6. Industrial robots can work twenty-four hours a day without a break, and highly complicated tasks can be done by them.

7. When she finished the speech, she was roundly applauded.

8. The president opposed the bill, but in the end it was signed by him anyway.

9. Poverty strangles hope, but ambition is stifled by wealth.

10. Though the attackers were vastly outnumbered, the battle was won by them.

14

VERBS
Mood

The **mood** of a verb or verb phrase indicates your attitude toward a particular statement as you are making it. Do you think of it as a statement of fact? Then you will use the indicative mood. Do you think of it as a command? Then you will use the imperative. Do you think of it as a wish, a recommendation, or a hypothetical condition? Then you will use the subjunctive.

14.1   The Indicative

The **indicative** is the mood used in most writing. It indicates that you are stating a fact or a strong probability.

> The George Washington Bridge *spans* the Hudson River.
> Orville and Wilbur Wright *are considered* authentic American heroes.
> We *have vacationed* in Tucson for three years.
> The bus *will depart* at 5:15 A.M.

14.2   The Imperative

The **imperative** mood indicates that you are giving an order or making a direct request:

> *Check* the oil.
> Please *send* me your latest catalog.
> *Don't forget* to write.
> *Let's finish* the job by noon.

As these examples show, you omit the subject if the mood of the verb in the sentence is imperative. When giving an order to others, you use the bare form of the verb. When you include yourself in the order, you use *let's* plus the bare form of the base verb.

14.3   The Subjunctive

The **subjunctive** mood indicates that you are stating a recommendation, a requirement, a request, a wish, or a condition that is contrary to fact. Statements in these categories require either a modal auxiliary or a subjunctive verb form.

Using Modal Auxiliaries

Modal auxiliaries are helping verbs that indicate the subjunctive mood. They include *can, could, may, might, must, should, would,* and *ought.* They are used in the ways listed here.

1. *Can* signifies possibility, capability, or permission:

> When enemies arm themselves, anything *can* happen.
> Few runners *can* do a mile in less than four minutes.
> Americans *can* visit Canada without a passport.

2. *Could* signifies possibility, a wish, or a contrary-to-fact condition:

> The roof *could* collapse any day now.
> Alice wished that she *could* swim.
> If lead *could* be turned into gold, gold would soon be worth no more than lead.

3. *May* signifies possibility or permission:

> Allison *may* agree to do the job.
> You *may* leave as soon as you complete your report.

4. *Might* signifies possibility:

> A delay in the delivery of fuel oil *might* cause hardships in many homes.

5. *Must* signifies a requirement or a conclusion:

> The survivors *must* be given food and water.
> Somewhere in outer space there *must* be life.

6. *Should* signifies probability, a recommendation, or an obligation:

> Interest rates *should* eventually come down.
> Musicians *should* practice every day.
> Partners *should* help each other.

7. *Would* signifies a wish or the result of a contrary-to-fact condition:

> Midwesterners wish that tornadoes *would* stop.
> If fleas were dollars, my dog *would* be a millionaire.

8. *Ought* signifies a recommendation or suggestion:

> The country *ought* to rehabilitate its railroads.

Ought is normally followed by an infinitive.

Using Subjunctive Verb Forms

1. Use the *present subjunctive* to state a recommendation or request:

> The dean recommends that Helen *drop* one of her courses.
> The principal requested that the children *be* quiet during the assembly.

A verb in the present subjunctive is written in the bare form (*drop, be*) with every subject. Compare the present subjunctive with the present indicative:

> INDICATIVE: Peter *exercises* every day.
> SUBJUNCTIVE: The doctor insists that Peter *exercise* every day.

> INDICATIVE: The children *were* noisy.
> SUBJUNCTIVE: The principal requested that they *be* quiet.

2. Use the *past subjunctive* to express a wish for something in the present:

> INDICATIVE: Joe *is* the president of our bowling club.
> SUBJUNCTIVE: He wishes he *were* the president of the United States.

> INDICATIVE: My cousin *lives* in Kansas.
> SUBJUNCTIVE: He wishes that he *lived* in California.

The past subjunctive is the same in form as the common past, except that for the verb *be,* the past subjunctive is *were* with every subject.

3. Use the *past perfect subjunctive* to express a wish for something in the past:

> INDICATIVE: I *saw* the 1980 World Series.
> SUBJUNCTIVE: I wish I *had seen* the 1979 World Series.

The past perfect subjunctive is the same in form as the common past perfect.

Subjunctive verb forms are sometimes used in conditional sentences, as discussed in the next section.

14.4 Forming Conditional Sentences

A conditional sentence normally consists of an *if* clause, which states a condition, and a result clause, which states the result of that condition. The mood of the verb in the *if* clause depends on the likelihood of the condition.

The Possible Condition

If the condition is likely or even barely possible, the mood of the verb in the *if* clause is indicative:

> [condition] If goldfish *are* put into cold water, [result] they will die.

The Impossible or Contrary-to-Fact Condition

If the condition is impossible or contrary to fact, the mood of the verb in the *if* clause is subjunctive, and the result clause usually includes a modal auxiliary, such as *would*. A condition contrary to present fact must be stated in the past subjunctive:

> [condition] If there *were* life on the moon, [result] it would have been discovered by now.

A condition contrary to past fact must be stated in the past perfect subjunctive:

> [condition] If Jimmy Carter *had been reelected* to the presidency in 1980, [result] Ronald Reagan would probably have retired from politics.

Name_____ Date_____

Exercise.   Recognizing Mood and Choosing the Appropriate Mood

Part A.   For each of the following sentences, identify in the blank at right the mood of the verb or verb phrase shown in italics.

EXAMPLE

Park only in the designated spaces.   _Imperative_

1. Don Mahler *works* for a local newspaper.   _____

2. Long *live* freedom!   _____

3. *Let's paint* the barn.   _____

4. My roommate wishes he *were* an eighteenth-century nobleman.   _____

5. Helen's German professor has recommended that she *study* in Munich next fall.   _____

6. Many economists argue that taxes *must be raised.*   _____

7. *Enclose* a check or money order with your application.   _____

8. If the earth *were* flat, the curious would find a way to peer over the edge.   _____

9. We *are* happy to have you with us.   _____

10. Our host has requested that we *be* punctual.   _____

Part B. In each of the following sentences, wherever a pair of verbs or auxiliaries is given in parentheses, choose the correct form and circle it. Then in the blank at right identify the mood of the verb or auxiliary you have chosen.

EXAMPLE

Gloria wishes that she (lives, (lived)) in Montreal.   *Subjunctive*

1. If I (was, were) you, I would apply for the job.   _____

2. Kindly (considers, consider) my application.   _____

3. The manager has directed that late arrivals (are, be) made to wait at the door until the intermission.   _____

4. If college tuition continues to rise at the present rate, the four-year cost of a residential college education (will, would) soon be more than $50,000.   _____

5. If the explorers (failed, had failed) to take a two-way radio with them, they would have been in danger when their vehicle broke down in the desert.   _____

6. The president has insisted that every department head (slashes, slash) his or her budget by twenty percent.   _____

7. Let us (works, work) together in peace and harmony.   _____

8. A large number of qualified teenagers cannot find jobs. A way (is, must be) found to give them employment.   _____

9. Every understudy wishes she (was, were) a leading lady.   _____

10. According to grandmother, children (shall, should) be respectful to their elders.   _____

15

DIRECT AND
INDIRECT REPORTING
OF DISCOURSE

Anything spoken or written can be reported in one of two ways: directly—by quotation of the actual words—or indirectly.

15.1 Direct Reporting of Statements— Using Quotation Marks

To report a statement directly, you must keep the words exactly as they are, and you must normally enclose them in **quotation marks**:

> ORIGINAL STATEMENT: I can take you as far as Denver.
> REPORTED STATEMENT: "I can take you as far as Denver."

To make the meaning of a reported statement clear and complete, you must often indicate who made it and to whom it was made. For this purpose you need a group of identifying words called a **tag**:

> "I can take you as far as Denver," the truck driver said to me.

(For more on how to punctuate quotations, see section 16.10, pp. 259-61.)

Placing Tags

If the quotation is short, the tag should be placed either just before or just after it:

> The truck driver said, "I can take you as far as Denver."
> "I can take you as far as Denver," said the truck driver.

If the quotation is more than a few words, the tag can often be placed in the middle of it. In this case, the tag should come between a subject and predicate, at the end of a phrase, or at the end of a clause:

> "Morality," writes Samuel Butler, "is the custom of one's country and the current feeling of one's peers."

"In a state of panic," notes Auden, "a man runs around in circles by himself."

"If a ride to Denver will help you," said the driver, "I can take you there."

"I'm headed to Denver," said the driver. "I can take you there."

Using Tenses in Tags

Since no statement can be reported until after it has been made, the verb in the tag is normally in the past tense:

"You've got a ride," the truck driver *said* to me.

But you may use the present when quoting a statement of lasting significance, and you must use the present when quoting a statement made by a literary character:

"Where there's marriage without love," writes Ben Franklin, "there will be love without marriage."

In Ralph Ellison's novel, the unnamed protagonist begins his story by saying, "I am an invisible man."

15.2   Indirect Reporting of Statements

When a statement is reported indirectly, no quotation marks are used:

ORIGINAL STATEMENT: I can take you as far as Denver.
DIRECT REPORT (QUOTATION): "I can take you as far as Denver."
INDIRECT REPORT: The man said that he could take me as far as Denver.

As this example shows, an indirect report does the following:

1. It refers to the person who made the reported statement.

2. It often puts *that* just before the statement. But *that* may be omitted:

The man said he could take me as far as Denver.

3. It changes the pronouns in the reported statement where necessary. In this example, *I* becomes *he,* and *you* becomes *me.*

4. It may change the tense of the verb in the reported statement. If the introductory verb is in the past tense, the verb in the reported statement may be in the past tense—even if the verb in the original was not. Thus, after *The man said,* which includes a past-tense verb, *I can take you* becomes *he could take me.* But if the original statement was recently made or has lasting significance, the original tense may be kept in the reported statement:

The governor said that property taxes *are crushing* the average homeowner.

The governor said that he *will cut* property taxes.

Samuel Butler wrote that the world *will* always *be governed* by self-interest.

15.3 Direct Reporting of Questions

To report a question directly, you normally use a verb of asking in the past tense:

> The man asked me, "Do you need a ride?"

Use the present tense for the verb of asking when you are reporting a question of standing importance or a question asked by a literary character:

> "What is life?" asks the biologist.
> In *The Brothers Karamazov*, Father Zossima asks, "What is hell?"

15.4 Indirect Reporting of Questions

In many respects the indirect reporting of questions resembles the indirect reporting of statements. But to report a question indirectly, you must normally introduce it with a past-tense verb of asking and a word like *who, what, whether, how, when, where, why,* or *if:*

> ORIGINAL QUESTION: Can you give me a lift?
> INDIRECT REPORT: I asked the man if he could give me a lift.
> ORIGINAL QUESTION: Where have you been?
> INDIRECT REPORT: I asked her where she had been.

As these examples show, you must change not only the pronouns but also the word order of the question: *Can you give me* becomes *if he could give me; have you been* becomes *she had been.* Also, the question mark at the end of the original question becomes a period. Do not write:

> *I asked the man if he could give me a lift?

As in the direct reporting of questions, use the present tense for the verb of asking when you report a question of standing importance or a question asked by a literary character:

> The biologist asks what life is.
> In *The Brothers Karamazov*, Father Zossima asks what hell is.

After a past-tense verb of asking, you must normally use a past tense in the reported question. Thus, *Can you give me* becomes *if he could give me; have you been* becomes *she had been.* But you may use the present tense if the reported question is essentially timeless:

> Archimedes wondered why objects float.

Name_____ Date_____

Exercise. Writing Direct and Indirect Reports

Using the information given in brackets, write a direct and an indirect report of each of the following statements and questions.

EXAMPLE

I like your singing. [*Speaker:* Priscilla; *listener:* me]

"I like your singing," Priscilla said to me.
Priscilla told me that she liked my singing.

1. Can I borrow your guitar? [*Speaker:* Nick; *listener:* Marcia]

2. I never lend my guitar to anyone. [*Speaker:* Marcia]

3. Have you finished your assignment? [*Speaker:* the teacher; *listener:* Frank]

4. I have finished half of it. [*Speaker:* Frank]

5. I am not feeling well. [*Speaker:* Frank]

6. How much will you give me for a gold bracelet? [*Speaker:* Barbara; *listener:* the man]

7. Male society's disparagement of woman has all the force of an unconscious conspiracy. [*Writer:* Betty Roszak]

8. A house divided against itself cannot stand. [*Writer:* Abraham Lincoln]

9. Oppressed people cannot remain oppressed forever. [*Writer:* Martin Luther King, Jr.]

10. Indians are probably invisible because of the tremendous amount of misinformation about them. [*Writer:* Vine Deloria, Jr.]

16

PUNCTUATION
AND
MECHANICS

16.1   The Period   •

1. Use a period to mark the end of a declarative sentence, a mild command, or an indirect question:

> DECLARATIVE SENTENCE: Synthetic fuels offer one solution to the energy crisis.
> MILD COMMAND: Join us if you can.
> INDIRECT QUESTION: I asked my instructor how we could measure the speed of light.

2. Use a period to mark the end of some abbreviations:

Ms. Black	8:30 A.M.
Mr. Grier	350 B.C.
Mrs. Rollins	24 Seaview Ave.
Dr. Davis	N.Y., N.Y.
Herbert Blough, Ph.D.	

Generally, you don't need periods when you abbreviate the names of organizations or when you use acronyms (pronounceable words formed from the initials of a multiword title):

RCA	HEW	NOW
ABC	SALT	UN

For guidance, see an up-to-date dictionary.

3. In general, do not use a period to make a sentence fragment:

> Traffic jams are frequent in the early morning and late afternoon. *Because many people still commute by car.

The period following *afternoon* is misused; it separates the independent clause about traffic jams from the subordinate clause beginning with *Because*. To correct the error, remove the period and do not capitalize *because:*

> Traffic jams are frequent in the early morning and late afternoon because many people still commute by car.

(For more on sentence fragments, see chapter 8, pp. 125–39.)

16.2   The Question Mark   ?

1. Use a question mark at the end of a direct question:

> Is man a rational creature?
> Has the rate of inflation declined appreciably in the last six months?

2. Use a question mark to indicate uncertainty within a statement:

> Old-timers still talk about a storm—in 1938?—that snapped the steeples of all three churches in town.

3. Do not use a question mark at the end of an indirect question:

> *Customers keep asking what the specials are?
> REVISED: Customers keep asking what the specials are.

16.3   The Exclamation Point   !

Use an exclamation point to mark the end of an exclamatory sentence, phrase, or word:

> The wanton destruction of wildlife must be stopped!
> Look out!

Name _____ Date _____

Exercise 1. Using Periods and Question Marks

Each of the following may need the addition or removal of one or more periods or question marks, or the substitution of one for the other. Where a period must be removed, you may also have to change capitalization. Circle any part of a sentence that includes an error in punctuation, and write the correction just below it. If a sentence is correct as it stands, write *Correct*.

EXAMPLE

I asked (Dr Brown) how long my leg would have to stay in a (cast?)

Dr. Brown   *cast.*

1. Sylvia screamed and struggled to get out of the crowd. Because

    she suffered from claustrophobia.

2. The finance committee wondered if turning down the thermo-

    stats would save enough money to balance the budget?

3. R P Blackmur was a distinguished literary critic who never earned

    a college degree.

4. Would you prefer to be called Miss Decato or Ms Decato.

5. When we came into the house, we were told to remove our shoes.

6. When one's rights are threatened by the government, is silence

    still golden.

7. She phoned to ask if Dr Logan could pull her aching tooth?

8. Don has not lived on Commonwealth Ave since 1979.

9. The committee rejected the recommendation. Even though it would have saved taxpayers thousands of dollars.

10. Jonathan led the singing of the alma mater. Because he was the only one who knew all the words.

16.4   The Comma ,

Using Commas

1. Use a comma to set off an introductory clause, phrase, or conjunctive adverb from the rest of the sentence:

> CLAUSE
> *If the sun shines,* we can picnic in the park.
> *When the president began speaking,* the reporters listened.
>
> PHRASE
> *Before turning in for the night,* we locked the windows and bolted the door.
> *To develop fluency in the spoken language,* students spend the winter term in Munich.
> *After a series of automobile accidents at the intersection of Main and South,* police installed a traffic light.
>
> CONJUNCTIVE ADVERB
> *On the other hand,* few voters want higher income taxes.
> *In fact,* they are disgusted with the present tax rates.
> *Consequently,* they have demanded tax cuts.

A conjunctive adverb may be a single word, such as *consequently,* or may itself be a phrase, such as *on the other hand.* For more on conjunctive adverbs, see pp. 71–72.

You may omit the comma after an introductory phrase if the phrase is short:

> *After the game* we all felt disappointed.

Normally you should not use a comma after an introductory conjunction, such as *but* or *so:*

> *But, we had a party anyway.
> REVISED: But we had a party anyway.

2. Use a comma before a conjunction that links two independent clauses. The conjunctions are *and, yet, or, but, nor, for,* and *so.*

> The children were playing various games, and the adults were relaxing with the Sunday paper.
> The workers decided to strike, for they saw no other way of getting a pay increase.

Do not use a comma when both of the clauses are short.

> The engine is old but it works.

3. Use a comma to join coordinate items in a series:

> The *clear, cold* air was invigorating. [adjectives preceding a noun]
> The volume includes *poems, stories, letters,* and *essays.* [nouns]
> The button may be hidden *inside a box, under a lamp, beneath a cushion,* or *in a fireplace.* [phrases]

After the accident Fran could not remember *where she was driving, what the road was like,* or *when she lost control of the car.* [clauses]

When a series includes three or more items, you normally need a conjunction between the last two. Use a comma before the conjunction, but not after it:

> *The truck skidded, slid over the edge of the road, and, tumbled down the embankment.
>
> REVISED: The truck skidded, slid over the edge of the road, and tumbled down the embankment.

You do not need a conjunction between adjectives preceding a noun, and you can sometimes omit the comma between two adjectives, especially when the first is a modifier of the second:

> Her pale green skirt fluttered in the breeze.

When items in a series are long or internally punctuated, use semicolons between them. (See p. 249.)

4. Use a comma or a pair of commas to set off a **nonrestrictive** modifier—a phrase or clause that does not restrict the meaning of its headword and is therefore not essential to the meaning of the sentence:

> The conductor, *pleased by the performance,* applauded his musicians.
> Most visitors to the nation's capital admire the Lincoln Memorial, *which is located in Potomac Park.*
> President Reagan, *who seems fully at ease before large audiences,* clearly enjoyed the rally at the Coliseum.

Do not use commas to set off a **restrictive** modifier—a phrase or clause that is essential to the meaning of its headword:

> All air-traffic controllers who went on strike were fired.

This clause restricts the meaning of its headword, *All air-traffic controllers.* Without the clause, the sentence would be saying something quite different—that all air-traffic controllers were fired. The *who* clause is therefore essential to the meaning of *All air-traffic controllers* and must not be set off from it by commas.

5. Use a comma or a pair of commas to set off a nonessential word or phrase, such as an absolute phrase, a phrase of contrast, an appositive, or a conjunctive adverb used in the middle of a clause:

> ABSOLUTE PHRASE
> The hero, *his fists clenched for battle,* ordered the villain to be gone by sundown.
> *Its sails flapping in the wind,* the schooner looked like a wounded sea gull.
>
> PHRASE OF CONTRAST
> She felt dazed, *not tired,* after the dance.

APPOSITIVE

Willie Mays, *a brilliant fielder and powerful hitter,* was elected to the National Baseball Hall of Fame in 1979.

The parade was led by Lorne Greene, *the TV star.*

CONJUNCTIVE ADVERB

No one in his right mind, *however,* would enter the tiger's cage.

6. Use a comma as needed with names, dates, and addresses.

Use a comma between parts of a name when the last name is given first, and between the whole name and any title, degree, or special designation:

Barringer, Francis
Betty Small, vice-president
Frank Dibble, Ph.D.
Joy Cohen, M.D.
John S. Wilson, Jr.

Use a comma to follow the greeting in a friendly or informal letter, and to follow the closing in a letter of any kind:

Dear Barbara,
Yours truly,
Yours respectfully,

Use a comma to set off successive items in a date or an address:

On July 5, 1887, the Blair family encountered a Sioux war party.
The Allyns now live at 8 Smith Street, Yarmouth, Maine.

Do not put a comma between the name of a month and the day, between a street number and the name of a street, or between the name of a state and the zip code:

*September, 24, 1980
REVISED: September 24, 1980

*7, York Street
REVISED: 7 York Street

*Galesburg, Illinois, 61401
REVISED: Galesburg, Illinois 61401

7. Use a comma in punctuating some quotations, as described on p. 259.

Name_____ Date_____

Exercise 2. Using Commas after Introductory Elements

Each of the following sentences may need a comma to set off an introductory clause, phrase, or conjunctive adverb. Circle the part of the sentence that needs a comma, and write the correction in the blank at right. If a sentence is correct as it stands, write *Correct*.

EXAMPLE

After Ellen backed the car out of the (garage she) discovered the flat tire.

garage, she

1. Silencing the crowd with a wave of his hand the smiling senator began his address.

  _____

2. However the smile soon faded from his face.

  _____

3. As they listened to the dire international news the crowd became somber.

  _____

4. When the speech was half over the senator switched to the country's domestic woes.

  _____

5. Grimly the people listened.

  _____

6. After he had finished speaking there was silence.

  _____

7. Softly a voice asked what the senator had been doing to allow the country to get into such a state.

   _____

8. Without the slightest show of hesitation the senator disclaimed any responsibility.

   _____

9. After a moment another person asked who was responsible.

   _____

10. Whenever the senator was asked that question he answered that big business was to blame.

   _____

Name_____Date_____

Exercise 3. Using Commas before Conjunctions

Each of the following sentences may need a comma before a conjunction. Circle the part of the sentence that needs a comma, and write the correction in the blank at right. If a sentence is correct as it stands, write *Correct*.

EXAMPLE

The sunset was (spectacular but) it failed to draw the children away from the television set.

spectacular, but

1. Christianity was introduced into Spain under the Romans but it did not become the official religion until the Visigoths established the Church there in 587.

   _____

2. A silk thread is finer than a human hair and it is stronger than a steel wire of the same thickness.

   _____

3. Robert had to swim twice as long as the other members of the team for he had missed a week of practice.

   _____

4. The twenty-five-foot waves of Hawaii give surfers a thrilling ride but most surfers have to settle for four-foot waves.

   _____

5. Silas was broke and his gas tank was empty. _____

6. Claudia broke her wrist playing tennis so she lost her chance to win the championship. _____

7. Maple sap was once gathered in buckets but now major producers of maple syrup run plastic tubing from tree to tree to catch the sap. _____

8. Memorization is tedious but it's often necessary. _____

9. Harry longed to leave his term paper unfinished for it was a beautiful day to play soccer. _____

10. A hush fell over the audience and the violins began the quiet third movement of the symphony. _____

Name _____ Date _____

Exercise 4. Using Commas to Join Items in a Series

Each of the following sentences may need one or more commas to join items in a series. Circle any part of a sentence that needs a comma, and write the correction just below it. If a sentence is correct as it stands, write *Correct*.

> EXAMPLE
>
> The drawer was stuffed with shirts sweaters socks and neckties.
>
> *shirts, sweaters, socks, and*

1. Watching the clouds sail by snoozing in the grass and staring in-

   to the water of the pond were Julie's favorite occupations for a

   summer day.

2. Andrew's palette knife was not in his desk in his locker or in the

   art room.

3. Gale's father was horrified when she charged to his account three

   jackets two pairs of shoes five pairs of jeans a sweater and a new

   coat.

4. Bill was fat because he ate lots of candy french fries and hot dogs.

5. The nurse gently cleaned the wound sprinkled it with anti-

   biotic powder and bandaged it.

6. Reading poetry and listening to Bach are Sam's favorite activities.

7. Thomas plays tennis squash and racquetball.

8. The new employee had obviously resolved to be on time to work

   hard and to leave his fellow workers strictly alone.

9. The coach asked Bob John and Alex to give the manager a hand

   with the equipment.

10. Geography of the Middle East Rat Psychology and Eskimos in

    Transition were the only courses still open.

Name _____ Date _____

Exercise 5. Using Commas with Nonrestrictive Modifiers

Each of the following sentences may need one or two commas to set off a nonrestrictive modifier. Circle any part of a sentence that needs a comma, and write the correction just below it. If a sentence is correct as it stands, write *Correct*.

EXAMPLES

My paternal (grandfather who) was born in (Ireland goes) every

       grandfather, who   *Ireland, goes*

year to the St. Patrick's Day parade in New York City.

My grandfather likes to think that everyone who wears green

on St. Patrick's Day is Irish.

Correct

1. The Great Wall of China completed in the third century B.C. is

   over two thousand miles long.

2. John Cage has earned a special place in the history of music by

   writing a piece that is totally silent for four minutes and thirty-

   three seconds.

3. The junk which is a common ship in the Orient has sails of matting.

4. Rudolph Periwinkle speaking for an hour and a half on the tadpole put most of the audience to sleep.

5. The CIA and the FBI which are our two main intelligence agencies have offices in every major city.

6. Not every tree that stays green all winter is a pine.

7. The chef and his two assistants working for twenty-six hours without a break managed to serve the seventeen-course dinner on time.

8. The deer sensing danger in the air suddenly bounded off.

9. The skunk lifting its tail threatened to spray us with its own special brand of perfume.

10. William A. Gold of England who wrote over three million words during a period of eighteen years earned only fifty cents for his writing in all that time.

Name _____ Date _____

Exercise 6.   Using Commas with Nonessential Words and Phrases

Each of the following sentences includes an absolute phrase, a phrase
of contrast, an appositive, or a conjunctive adverb. Circle any part of
a sentence that needs a comma, and write the correction just below
it. If a sentence is correct as it stands, write *Correct.*

EXAMPLE

Casey (Stengel onetime) manager of the New York (Yankees had)

    Stengel, onetime   Yankees, had

his own special way of mangling the English language.

1. The president of the club however forgot to attend the meeting.

2. The beautiful snake not the ugly one proved to be poisonous.

3. Their voices raised to fever pitch the protesters threw a shower

   of rocks and then stormed the building.

4. Columbus sailed in a caravel a small sailing vessel with three or

   four masts and a high narrow poop.

5. Mata Hari the famous spy of World War I was executed by the

   French.

6. The defendant his story demolished under cross-examination finally broke down and confessed everything.

7. Asteroids more properly called planetoids orbit the sun along with the planets.

8. Johannes Kepler one of the greatest astronomers of all time discovered three basic laws of planetary motion.

9. An ordinary three-speed bicycle, for instance, now costs more than eighty dollars.

10. Janice wanted the blue plaid coat not the red one.

Name_____ Date _____

Exercise 7.   Using Commas with Names, Dates, and Addresses

Each of the following sentences includes a name, date, or address. Circle any part of a sentence that needs a comma, and write the correction just below it. If a sentence is correct as it stands, write *Correct*.

EXAMPLE

On (December 7 1941) the Japanese bombed Pearl Harbor.

December 7, 1941,

1. General Daniel Morgan led the Americans to one of the most

   brilliant victories of the Revolutionary War in a battle near

   Cowpens South Carolina.

2. The British House of Commons passed a bill freeing all slaves in

   Britain and its colonies on August 7 1833.

3. Molly Bloom lives at 7 Eccles Street Dublin Ireland.

4. Captain John Smith was an English adventurer born in Willoughby

   England.

5. He was baptized there on January 6 1580.

6. John Smith helped found Jamestown Virginia in 1607.

7. He died on June 21, 1631.

8. The lecturer was Henry Tielman Ph.D.

9. The Robertsons' new address is 5 Valley Road San Mateo California.

10. The best essay was submitted by Louis J. Pastene Jr.

Misusing Commas

The comma can be misused in many ways. The three most common ways require special notice.

1. Do not use a comma by itself to join two independent clauses:

> *I can't study well at home, the phone keeps ringing.

Use a semicolon, a period, or a comma plus a conjunction:

> I can't study well at home; the phone keeps ringing.
> I can't study well at home. The phone keeps ringing.
> I can't study well at home, for the phone keeps ringing.

(For more on the comma splice, see section 4.6, p. 81.)

2. In general, do not use a comma between a subject and its predicate:

> *The recommendations of the manager, will probably be approved.
> REVISED: The recommendations of the manager will probably be approved.

> *Five of the musicians, have the flu.
> REVISED: Five of the musicians have the flu.

Commas between a subject and its predicate should be used only in pairs, to set off a nonessential word, phrase, or clause from the rest of the sentence:

> Frank Helms, who was injured in the first quarter, could not play in the second half.

3. Do not use a comma between a conjunction and the last item in a series:

> *At the beach we swam, surfed, and, built sand castles.
> REVISED: At the beach we swam, surfed, and built sand castles.

Name_____ Date _____

Exercise 8.   Eliminating Misused Commas

Each of the following sentences may include a misused comma. Circle the part of the sentence where a comma has been misused, and write the correction just below it, adding a conjunction after the comma, substituting another punctuation mark, or removing the comma, as necessary. If a sentence is correct as it stands, write *Correct*.

EXAMPLE

A car with bad (brakes, is) a menace.

brakes is

1. Social psychologists, seek to discover the reasons people act the

   way they do.

2. In the United States sociology has become an accepted subject

   at most universities and colleges, in the nations of Africa and

   Asia very little or no sociology is studied.

3. The boy in the blue blazer, knows all about using commas.

4. In soccer, players may not hold, push, shove, kick, strike, or,

   trip opposing players.

5. Using a comma without a good reason, is a mistake.

6. He was brilliant at remembering names, making speeches, and, charming his audiences.

7. Writing well depends on careful rewriting, bursts of creativity are not enough.

8. Some of the crustaceans' appendages are used for gathering food; the rest are for walking.

9. Vinyl floors are durable, waterproof, and, easily cleaned.

10. Colin's finger-snapping, annoyed the waiter.

Name_____ Date _____

Exercise 9. Review: Using Commas

In the following passage, some commas are misused and others are
missing. Remove any misused comma, substitute another punctuation
mark if necessary, and change capitalization as required. As you make
these corrections, write out the passage in full, keeping each line of
your revision just below the corresponding line of the original.

EXAMPLE

As a result of the hurricane many families were

As a result of the hurricane, many families were

homeless, they slept in tents makeshift shelters and caves.

homeless; they slept in tents, makeshift shelters, and caves.

1   The *Guinness Book of World Records* is a rich fabulous

2   and fascinating source of information. In this book

3   which is published every year you will find pictures

4   of the world's tallest smallest and, fattest human

5   beings, furthermore, you can learn who won the

6   world's longest marathon dance in 1932 where to

7   find the world's deepest mine and what, the hottest

8   spice is. Some of the feats, described in this book,

9 are truly amazing. In 1958 for example Mrs. Mary E. Davis

10 talked nonstop for more than 110 hours jabbering

11 away from September 2 to September 7. In

12 1973 a man, named Henri Rochetain balanced himself

13 for 185 days on a wire, suspended eighty-two feet

14 above a supermarket in St. Etienne France, while

15 he was on the wire he, walked some 310 miles and,

16 somehow managed to sleep as well. In 1978 John

17 Massis a Belgian used a bit between his teeth to

18 pull three railroad cars, that together weighed

19 140 tons. Why do people, do these crazy things?

20 The answer is simple, they each want a place

21 in the *Guinness Book of World Records.*

16.5   The Semicolon   ;

1. Use a semicolon to join two independent clauses that are closely related in meaning:

> Some visitors thrive on activities; others seldom leave the lounge.
> We seem to lack a sense of direction; we move from one distraction to another instead of advancing steadily to a well-defined goal.

2. Use a semicolon to join two independent clauses when the second begins with or includes a conjunctive adverb, such as *however, for example,* or *in addition:*

> Everyone agrees that nuclear warfare is horrible; the great powers, however, continue to manufacture nuclear weapons.
> Renfrew is creative and independent; for example, he designed his own house.

3. Use a semicolon between items in a series when one or more of the items include commas:

> The furniture consisted of a sofa with three large, shapeless cushions; four matching wooden chairs with upright backs; and a corner cupboard imported from Bristol, England.

4. Do not use a semicolon between a phrase and the clause to which it belongs:

> *The bride and groom moved slowly down the aisle; smiling all the way.

Instead, use a comma:

> The bride and groom moved slowly down the aisle, smiling all the way.

When the phrase is prepositional, the comma may sometimes be omitted—especially when the phrase follows the verb:

> The bride and groom moved slowly down the aisle with smiling faces.

5. Do not use a semicolon between a subordinate clause and the main clause:

> *Even though I was exhausted; I drove for three hours.

Instead, use a comma:

> Even though I was exhausted, I drove for three hours.

When the subordinate clause follows the main clause, the comma may be omitted:

> I drove for three hours even though I was exhausted.

6. Do not use a semicolon to introduce a list:

> *Her house has four rooms; a kitchen, a parlor, a bedroom, and a bathroom.

Instead, use a colon:

> Her house has four rooms: a kitchen, a parlor, a bedroom, and a bathroom.

Name _____ Date _____

Exercise 10.   Using Semicolons

Each of the following sentences may need the addition or removal of one or more semicolons. Circle any part of a sentence that includes an error in punctuation, and write the correction in the blank at right. If a sentence is correct as it stands, write *Correct*.

EXAMPLE

The tornado had leveled the (house it) was nothing but a heap of rubble.   *house; it*

1. Gordon traveled across Russia on the Trans-Siberian Railroad, as a result, he saw much more of the country than the average tourist does.   _____

2. The Ku Klux Klan is reviving no one knows exactly why.   _____

3. The daring Phoenicians held their place as leading sea traders for several centuries they sailed through the Mediterranean, into the Atlantic, and north to the Baltic Sea.   _____

4. Ron's team had several weaknesses; lack of leadership, lack of cooperation, and lack of determination.   _____

5. The troops marched through rain, snow, and hail; then they crawled through mud.   _____

6. Laughing until he was weak; Ian staggered out of the theater.

        _____

7. We have been traveling for days; with little water and no food.

        _____

8. Tyler wears his old sweater; though he has a new red one.

        _____

9. Delegates came from Dallas, Texas, Butte, Montana, Mobile, Alabama, and Atlanta, Georgia.

        _____

10. The army launched a new rocket, ordered new rifles; and established a new training camp in Georgia.

        _____

16.6   The Colon   :

1. Use a colon to introduce a list or an explanation directly related to something just mentioned:

> The tenants broke two of the appliances: the washing machine and the electric oven.
> The miser had only one desire: to see his gold coins.

Do not use a colon to introduce a list when the items follow a form of *be (are, were, will be)* or a preposition, such as *of:*

> *The three best players on the team are: Hill, West, and Adams.
> REVISED: The three best players on the team are Hill, West, and Adams.

> *The fabric consists of: cotton, nylon, and Dacron.
> REVISED: The fabric consists of cotton, nylon, and Dacron.

2. Use a colon to introduce a quotation (usually of more than one line) in an essay:

> In the concluding chapter of *Walden,* Thoreau declares: "If a man does not keep pace with his companions, perhaps it is because he hears a different drummer. Let him step to the music which he hears, however measured or far away."

3. Use a colon after the salutation in a formal letter:

> Dear Senator Grant:
> Dear Ms. Whipple:
> To Whom It May Concern:

4. Use a colon to separate hours from minutes when the time of day is shown in numerals:

> 7:30   12:05   6:45

16.7   The Dash   —

1. Use a dash to introduce a word, phrase, or clause that summarizes the words preceding it:

> The film showed grizzlies, wolves, caribou, and bighorn sheep—all animals threatened by man.

2. Use a pair of dashes to set off an interruption that is closely relevant to a sentence but not grammatically part of it:

> Her hatred of the old school building—she had been ridiculed by her classmates—led her to leave the neighborhood as soon as she could.

In typing, make a dash with two hyphens (- -) and leave no space on either side.

16.8 Parentheses ( )

1. Use parentheses to enclose words, phrases, or complete sentences that offer a side comment or help to clarify a point:

> Joe DiMaggio's hitting streak (he batted safely in fifty-six consecutive games) may never be surpassed.

A parenthesized sentence that appears within another sentence does not need a capital or a period.

2. Use parentheses to enclose numerals or letters introducing the items of a list:

> The essay has three main sections: (a) an introduction summarizing the history of industrial strife in the mine, (b) an analysis of present working conditions, and (c) a proposal for major reforms.

3. Use parentheses to enclose numerals clarifying or confirming a spelled-out number:

> The rent is eighty-five dollars ($85.00) a week.

16.9 Brackets [ ]

1. Use brackets to insert a clarifying detail, comment, or correction of your own into a passage written by someone else:

> According to the author, "The cause of the war can be traced to the jealousy of Aphrodite [the goddess of love], for she would tolerate no rivals."

If you wish to call attention to a misspelling in the quoted material, use the Latin word *sic* ("thus"), or give the correct spelling within the brackets:

> "On the other hand, Aphrodite could be generous with the mortils [*sic*] that worshipped her." [or] "On the other hand, Aphrodite could be generous with the mortils [mortals] that worshipped her."

Typewriters do not normally include keys for brackets. You may either put the brackets in by hand or construct them by using the slash and underlining keys: [ ]

2. Do not use brackets when inserting comments into your own writing. Use parentheses or dashes.

Name_____ Date_____

Exercise 11.   Using Colons, Dashes, Parentheses, and Brackets

Some of the following sentences may need the addition or removal
of a colon. Others may need brackets, parentheses, or dashes. Circle
any part of a sentence that includes an error in punctuation, and write
the correction just below it. If a sentence is correct as it stands, write
Correct.

EXAMPLES

The hostages wanted just one (thing freedom) to go home.

thing: freedom

For lunch we had a platter (of: cold) turkey, ham, salami, and

of cold

lettuce.

1. The plane was due to land at 9 30.

2. La Rochefoucauld states "Nothing is as contagious as example,

   and we never perform an outstandingly good or evil action with-

   out its producing others of its sort."

3. The virtuosity of Heifetz his playing was incomparably brilliant

   made other violinists want to throw their instruments away.

4. In his short lifetime he died at thirty-six Mozart produced an enormous quantity of music.

5. Georgina and Nick met in the lobby at 4 15.

6. The audience all five hundred of them dashed for the door when someone screamed, "Fire!"

7. In New York we went to the World Trade Center, to the Museum of Modern Art we saw the new wing, and to Central Park.

8. Gleitman says: "They certain animals and birds have fewer offspring, but they then see to it that most of their brood survives into maturity."

9. Gleitman continues: "They the parents feed them, clean them, shelter them, and protect them during some initial period of dependency."

10. The doctor ordered a new regime no smoking, no drinking, plenty of exercise, and a diet.

Name _____ Date _____

11. Mr. O'Malley he was fat, flushed, and fifty protested that it was

    quite impossible for him to give up all his pleasures.

12. Jim's favorite desserts are: hot fudge sundaes, strawberry short-

    cake, and apple pie.

13. The service began at 10:30.

14. Dear Senator Kennedy

    Could I have an appointment to see you next week?

15. Little Sam's favorite hero is "Spidder *sic* Man."

16.10   Quotation Marks and Quoting   " "

Double Quotation Marks

1. Use double quotation marks (" ") to enclose any words, phrases, or short passages quoted from speech or written matter:

> Ambrose Bierce defines a coward as "one who in a perilous emergency thinks with his legs."
>
> The secretary of state said that evidence of Soviet involvement in the guerrilla war was "extensive."

2. Use double quotation marks to set off certain titles (as specified in section 16.17, pp. 276–77).

3. Do not use quotation marks for emphasis. Quotation marks can actually weaken a statement. For example:

> She spoke with "glowing" enthusiasm. [TRANSLATION: She was putting on an act.]

Single Quotation Marks

Use single quotation marks (' ') to enclose a quotation within a quotation:

> "Patrick Henry," said the teacher, "was a fiery orator. It was he who declared, 'Give me liberty, or give me death.'"

Punctuating Quotations

1. Use a comma or a colon to introduce a quotation:

> Karen said, "I'm going home."
>
> John Holt writes: "The first and worst thing we do is to make children anxious about spelling."

Most writers use a comma to introduce quoted speech and a colon to introduce quoted writing. But you need neither a comma nor a colon to introduce a quoted word or phrase:

> My mother said she was "sick and tired" of our constant complaining.

2. Use a comma to mark the end of a quoted sentence that is followed by an identifying tag:

> "I'm going home," said Karen.
>
> "I'll stay," said Margaret. "Phil and I haven't finished our conversation."

3. Use a pair of commas to set off a tag that interrupts a quoted sentence, whether spoken or written:

> "In the first place," said Carl, "the car isn't mine."
>
> "The first and worst thing we do," writes Holt, "is to make children anxious about spelling."

The second part of the quotation does not begin with a capital letter because it does not begin a new sentence. It completes the sentence that was interrupted by the tag.

4. Use a period to mark the end of a quoted statement that is not followed by a tag:

> Karen said, "I'm going home."

5. When you use a comma or a period at the end of a quotation, put it inside the closing quotation mark:

> "Give me liberty," said Patrick Henry, "or give me death."

6. When you use a semicolon or a colon at the end of a quotation, put it outside the closing quotation mark:

> The manager said that my chance of getting a raise was "slight"; nevertheless, I decided to stay on the job.
>
> Explaining the company balance sheet, the treasurer cited "major setbacks": a prolonged strike, the loss of a million-dollar lawsuit, and an explosion at one of the plants.

7. When you use a question mark or an exclamation point at the end of a quotation, put it inside the closing quotation mark only if it belongs to the quotation; otherwise, put it outside:

> He asked me, "Where are you going?"
> "Help!" she cried.
> What does the president mean when he speaks of the "truly needy"?

Wherever you put the question mark or the exclamation point, do not use a period with it:

> *He asked me, "Where are you going?".
> REVISED: He asked me, "Where are you going?"

Quoting Poetry

If you quote more than a single line of poetry, you must show where one line ends and another begins. Use a slash (/), with a space on each side, to mark the division:

> Emily Dickinson wrote, "Because I could not stop for death, / He kindly stopped for me."

If you quote more than two lines of poetry, use indentation instead of quotation marks, as described next in "Quoting Long Passages."

Quoting Long Passages

1. To quote more than four lines of prose or more than two lines of poetry, use indentation instead of quotation marks. Introduce the quotation with a colon, leave a double space, indent the whole quotation at least five spaces, and double-space the quotation itself:

Peter Farb has this to say about the process of falling
asleep:

> A number of curious experiences occur at the onset of
>
> sleep. A person just about to go to sleep may experi-
>
> ence an electric shock, a flash of light, or a crash
>
> of thunder--but the most common sensation is that of
>
> floating or falling, which is why "falling asleep" is
>
> a scientifically valid description.

2. When a passage you indent contains quoted matter of its own, pre-
serve the double quotation marks around that, as shown in the preceding example.

3. When the lines of poetry are short, center them on the page:

> One of Emily Brontë's poems ends with this stanza:
>
> > Hope--whose whisper would have given
> >
> > Balm to all that frenzied pain--
> >
> > Stretched her wings and soared to heaven;
> >
> > Went--and ne'er returned again!

Name _____ Date _____

Exercise 12.   Using Quotation Marks

Revise any of the following sentences in which quotation marks are needed. If a sentence is correct as it stands, write *Correct*.

EXAMPLE

Patrick Henry, said the teacher, was a fiery orator. It was he who declared, Give me liberty, or give me death.

"Patrick Henry," said the teacher, "was a fiery orator. "It was he who declared, 'give me liberty, or give me death.'"

1. I've got a closet full of clothes, said Christy mournfully, but nothing to wear.

2. Interest rates have to come down sometime, the banker said.

3. The vilest abortionist, says George Bernard Shaw, is he who attempts to mold a child's character.

4. If you want to economize, the salesman observed, you should install an efficient heating system.

5. Martin's watercolors can be called, as one critic remarked, imaginative yet realistic.

6. When a scoundrel talks about honest endeavors, you had better walk away.

7. In her book about the minds of children, Margaret Donaldson says, The child has a natural tendency to vocalize randomly himself.

8. When a woman tells the truth, says Adrienne Rich in one of her books, she is creating the possibility for more truth around her.

9. What, he asked, do psychologists mean when they say that someone is a manic-depressive?

10. On Friday, the instructor announced, we will discuss the poetry of Whitman.

Name_____ Date_____

Exercise 13.   Punctuating Quotations

Revise any of the following sentences in which a direct quotation is incorrectly punctuated. If a sentence is correct as it stands, write *Correct*.

EXAMPLE

As soon as we get home Roberta said I'm going to take a hot shower.

"As soon as we get home," Roberta said, "I'm going to take a hot shower."

1. I only regret that I have but one life to lose for my country said Nathan Hale.

2. If the assassins had known they were going to get killed the reporter commented they might not have been so enthusiastic about the job.

3. Cleo asked, "Which of these men led the strike?"

4. "Following the meeting" the chairman said, "there will be a coffee hour in the lounge."

5. Who does he think he is Terry asked Arnold.

6. New Zeus detergent leaves your wash smelling oh-so fresh cooed the announcer.

7. The new play is charming and sophisticated said the *Daily News*.

8. As long as we can keep peace the secretary sighed I guess I'll attend any meeting they propose.

9. I lost my paper wailed Jeremy and I've thrown away my notes and my first draft.

10. It is not my aim to silence the opposition the captain said sternly but to hear them out.

16.11   Ellipsis Dots   . . .

1. Use three spaced dots—

    1. To signal the omission of a word or words from the middle of a quoted sentence:

        "No high-minded man . . . can contemplate the lumbering and slovenly lying of the present day without grieving to see a noble art so prostituted."   —Samuel L. Clemens

    2. To signal hesitation or halting speech in dialogue:

        "But . . . you can't leave us," she gasped.

2. Use four spaced dots—

    1. To show that you are omitting the end of a quoted sentence:

        "No fact is more firmly established than that lying is a necessity of our circumstances. . . . "   —Samuel L. Clemens

    The fourth dot is the closing period.

    2. To show that you have omitted one or more whole sentences:

        "The trend of our epoch up to this time has been consistently towards specialism and professionalism. . . . Now, if this world of ours were really what is called reasonable, I do not know that there would be any fault to find with this."   —G. K. Chesterton

Whenever you omit part of a quoted passage, you should be careful not to leave out anything that could be considered essential to the meaning of the passage.

16.12   The Slash   /

1. Use a slash, or virgule, to indicate alternative words:

    Every member of the committee should bring his/her report to the meeting.

2. Use a slash to mark off lines of poetry when you run them on as if they were prose, as described on p. 260.

3. Use a slash in typing a fraction that is not on one of your typewriter keys:

    5 7/8   15/16

16.13.   The Hyphen   –

1. Use a hyphen to divide a word at the end of a line:

    Unfortunately, the rocket did not reach its destina-
tion.

–

The word should be divided at the end of a syllable. If you aren't sure what the syllables of a word are, see your dictionary.

2. Use a hyphen to form a compound noun or a compound modifier:

> George C. Marshall was a soldier-statesman.
> A world-famous singer will attend the concert.
> The children were raised in a two-room cabin.
> My uncle is taking a round-the-world trip.

3. Use a hyphen to join a prefix to a proper noun or proper adjective:

> Political turmoil characterized the immediate post-Revolutionary period.
> Non-Catholics will be welcome at the service.

4. Use a hyphen in a number written as two words, provided the number is below one hundred:

> Three-quarters of the field is under water.
> The collection includes twenty-two stamps from Greece.

Do not use a hyphen with numbers greater than ninety-nine:

> Two hundred guests have been invited.

Name_____ Date_____

Exercise 14.   Using Slashes and Hyphens

Each of the following sentences includes terms that may require one
or more slashes or hyphens. Where a slash or hyphen is missing, circle
the incorrect form, and write the correct form in the blank at right.
If a sentence is correct as it stands, write *Correct*.

EXAMPLE

I've already finished (one half) of the
assignment.   *one-half*

1. In parts of rural America, the one-
    room schoolhouse has made a come-
    back.   _____

2. Historians know little about preCo-
    lumbian life in America.   _____

3. This is certainly an either or situation!   _____

4. Jan's mother did not believe that a ten
    year old girl was capable of choosing
    all her own clothes.   _____

5. Nine tenths of the doctor's patients
    said the same thing.   _____

6. The plane fare to Atlantic City was
    ninety six dollars.   _____

7. Like Wordsworth, he had "traveled among unknown men, In lands beyond the sea." _____

8. Bryant did not realize that he had to compete against world ranking skiers. _____

9. The beady eyed gambler studied his cards. _____

10. Who wrote, "I think that I shall never see A poem lovely as a tree"? _____

16.14   The Apostrophe   ,

1. Use an apostrophe to mark the omission of a letter or letters in a contraction:

FULL FORM	CONTRACTION
We do not swim.	We don't swim.
I have eaten.	I've eaten.
She would not speak.	She wouldn't speak.
It is raining now.	It's raining now.

It's is the contraction of *it is*. Don't confuse *it's* with *its*, meaning "belonging to it," as in *The gate is swinging on its hinges.*

2. Use an apostrophe to help form the possessive of some nouns and pronouns referring to persons and animals:

1. If the noun is singular, add an apostrophe and *-s:*

   child's
   Mary's
   Charles's
   everybody's
   dog's

2. If the noun is plural and the plural spelling ends in *-s*, add just the apostrophe:

   soldiers'
   the Smiths'

3. If the plural spelling does not end in *-s*, add an apostrophe and *-s:*

   children's
   women's

4. To indicate joint possession, add the apostrophe, and the *-s* if necessary, to the second of two nouns:

   Mark and Tara's silver anniversary
   John and his sisters' legacy

5. When using a compound, add the apostrophe, and the *-s* if necessary, to the last word:

   brother-in-law's family

3. In general, do not use an apostrophe and *-s* to form the possessive of nouns naming inanimate objects or abstract ideas:

   *the kitchen's floor
   the floor of the kitchen

   *the experiment's results
   the results of the experiment

4. Do not use an apostrophe with a possessive pronoun. The possessive pronouns are spelled as follows:

> my, mine
> your, yours
> his
> her, hers
> its
> our, ours
> their, theirs

5. Use an apostrophe to help form the plural of a numeral, a letter, or a word treated as a word:

> three 8's   two *t*'s
> the 1930's two *why*'s

Some writers are beginning to drop the apostrophe when writing the plural of a numeral or letter:

> three 8s   two *t*s
> the 1930s

Name _____ Date _____

Exercise 15.   Using Apostrophes

Each of the following sentences may need an apostrophe or may include one that is misused. Circle the part of the sentence that includes an error, and write the correction in the blank at right. If a sentence is correct as it stands, write *Correct*.

EXAMPLE

The accident broke (Marias) leg.   *Maria's* _____

1. Everybody's business is nobodys business.   _____

2. The Carmichaels parties always drew big crowds.   _____

3. The speech's ending left the audience stunned.   _____

4. The dog put it's muddy paws all over my new skirt.   _____

5. The battle for womens liberation has been waged on many fronts.   _____

6. I wondered whether I would be invited to Sharon and Cliffs wedding.   _____

7. But I really didn't care.   _____

8. The childrens shouts echoed down the corridors.   _____

9. Massive layoffs in the auto industry signaled the recession's beginning.
   _____

10. The company finally met the workers demands.
    _____

11. Ive never eaten raw oysters, but I'd like to try them sometime.
    _____

12. Sometimes its hard to remember when to use the apostrophe.
    _____

13. Richard Nixons presidency ended with his resignation.
    _____

14. Byrons life was packed with adventure.
    _____

15. The dog's bite turned out to be much worse than it's bark.
    _____

16. From below we heard the fishermens voices.
    _____

17. My parents wouldnt let me watch TV on school nights.
    _____

18. My sister-in-laws birthday party lasted until 3 A.M.
    _____

19. Laura's serve is stronger than Ellens.
    _____

20. Theres no point in waiting; we must act now.
    _____

16.15   Capitalization   *cap/lc*

1. Capitalize the first word of a sentence:

> The specialty of the house is a fish chowder.
> When did the geese migrate?
> Please enclose payment with your order.

2. Capitalize, with a few exceptions, the words in a proper noun, such as the name of a person, a specific place, a firm or other organization, or a special event:

Dwight D. Eisenhower	Camp Pocco	Mobil Corporation
Susan B. Anthony	Sussex County	Independence Day
Chicago	Knights of	World Series
Quebec	Columbus	Tanglewood Music
Lake Superior	Board of Selectmen	Festival
Death Valley	General Motors	

As these examples show, a word like *Lake, Valley, County,* or *Corporation* is capitalized when it forms part of an official name.

3. Capitalize the first word in a line of poetry, unless the poet uses lower case:

> I've stayed in the front yard all my life.
> I want a peek at the back
> Where it's rough and untended and hungry weed grows.
> A girl gets sick of a rose.
>
> —Gwendolyn Brooks

> I am the hope of your unborn,
> truly, when there is no more of me . . .
> there shall be no more of you. . . .
>
> —Conrad Kent Rivers

4. Capitalize certain words in titles (as specified in section 16.17, pp. 276-77).

5. Capitalize the pronoun *I* wherever you use it:

> I have not said I would take the job.
> Do I need to have another interview?

16.16   Italics and Underlining for Italics   *ital*

Most of this book is set in ordinary type (known as "roman"), but you've no doubt already noticed that we have been using *italic type* for distinction and emphasis *(this is an example of italic type).* You may need to use italics in your own writing, but if you are using a pen or pencil or standard typewriter, you cannot readily produce words in italic lettering. You can, however, represent italics by under-lining.

1. Use italics to emphasize a word or phrase in a statement:

> The most fundamental kind of love, which underlies all types of love, is <u>brotherly love</u>.   -Erich Fromm

2. Use italics to identify a letter or a word treated as a word:

> <u>Parallel</u> has three <u>l</u>'s, two of which resemble parallel train tracks.

3. Use italics to identify a foreign word or phrase not yet absorbed into English:

> They lived in a quiet little <u>cul-de-sac</u> off the main street.

4. Use italics to identify the name of a ship, an airplane, or the like.

> <u>Mayflower</u> [ship]
> <u>Voyager 2</u> [spacecraft]
> <u>Cape Codder</u> [train]

5. Use italics for certain titles (as specified in the next section).

16.17 Titles *title*

1. Capitalize the first and the last word of a title, whatever they are, and all the words in between except articles (such as *a* and *the*), prepositions (such as *for, among,* and *to*), and conjunctions (such as *and, but,* and *or*):

> <u>The Turn of the Screw</u> [book]
> <u>I Knock at the Door</u> [book]
> "Home on the Range" [song]
> "Leda and the Swan" [poem]
> "Where College Fails Us" [essay]

2. Use italics for the title of a book, magazine, scholarly journal, newspaper, government report, play, musical, opera or other long musical composition, film, television show, radio program, or long poem:

> <u>The Uses of Enchantment</u> [book]
> <u>Sports Illustrated</u> [magazine]
> <u>Boston Globe</u> [newspaper]
> <u>A Raisin in the Sun</u> [play]
> <u>My Fair Lady</u> [musical]
> <u>Otello</u> [opera]
> <u>Raging Bull</u> [film]
> <u>Dallas</u> [televison show]
> <u>Morning Pro Musica</u> [radio program]
> <u>The Prelude</u> [long poem]

3. Use quotation marks for the title of a short work, such as a magazine article, short story, short poem, song, or chapter in a book:

> "Shelters on the Plains" [magazine article]
> "Big Boy Leaves Home" [short story]
> "Trees" [short poem]
> "Home on the Range" [song]
> "Higher Laws" [chapter in a book]

4. In general, do not use italics or quotation marks when you write your own title at the head of a story, poem, or essay:

> Cats in the Cellar
> Twilight in Nevada
> Problems in Suburbia

Use italics or quotation marks in your own title only when you refer to another title:

> Reporting in the Boston Globe
> Violence in Raging Bull
> Symbolism in "Big Boy Leaves Home"

Name_____ Date _____

Exercise 16. Using Capitalization and Italics, and Writing Titles

Part A. In each of the following sentences, draw a single line under any word that needs italics, and three lines under any letters that need capitalization. If a sentence is correct as it stands, write *Correct.*

> **EXAMPLES**
>
> <u>we</u> spent our vacation at <u>atlantic</u> <u>city</u>.
>
> <u>why</u> does the word <u>sex</u> make some people giggle?

1. the words liberal and conservative have been defined in many different ways.

2. i have always wanted to ride over niagara falls in a barrel.

3. Michelle spent the afternoon at a bowling alley in Tulsa.

4. chicago is my favorite city.

5. I can never remember how to spell *separate.*

6. the popularity of japanese cars has sharply reduced the sale of american ones.

7. the 1980 olympic games were held in moscow.

8. who understands anyone else perfectly?

9. some years ago, an englishman named francis chichester sailed around the world alone in a fifty-three-foot bermuda-rigged yacht named gipsy moth IV.

10. roberta and david took their children to disneyland.

Part B. Write out correctly each of the following titles, adding capitalization and italics or quotation marks as necessary.

EXAMPLE

where college fails us [magazine article]

1. the last tycoon [novel]

2. blowin' in the wind [song]

3. a chorus line [musical]

4. scientific american [magazine]

5. writing—a college handbook [book]

6. quincy patriot ledger [newspaper]

7. the beast in the jungle [short story]

8. why i write [essay]

9. the taming of the shrew [play]

10. the damnation of faust [opera]

16.18   Abbreviations   *ab*

1. Use abbreviations for most titles accompanying a name:

Dr. Carol Smith	John S. Hilson, Jr.
Ms. Brenda Green	Nancy Black, Ph.D.
Mr. George Flynt	Peter Decker, M.D.
BUT: Miss Florence Matthews	Roberta Crown, D.D.

But use the full titles when referring to religious, governmental, and military leaders:

the Reverend William Sloan Coffin
Senator John Tower
General Robert E. Lee

2. Use abbreviations for the terms that help to specify a date or a time of day:

44 B.C.	7:30 A.M.
A.D. 1620	9:30 P.M.

3. You may use abbreviations in referring to well-known firms and other organizations:

TWA	AFL-CIO
UNESCO	NBC

Abbreviations like these are used without periods.

4. Use abbreviations to designate certain units of measurement when they are accompanied by numerals:

35 mph (or m.p.h.)   28 mpg (or m.p.g.)   78 rpm (or r.p.m.)

5. In general, do not use abbreviations in formal writing for the days of the week, the months of the year, academic subjects, geographical and political entities, and units of measurement not accompanied by numerals:

Monday	biology	New England	two feet
October	history	The Rocky Mountains	six inches

Many writers do now use *U.S.A.* for *United States of America* and *U.S.S.R.* for *Union of Soviet Socialist Republics*. You may also use *Mt.* before the name of a mountain, as in *Mt. Rainier,* and *St.* in the name of a place, as in *St. Joseph.*

16.19   Numbers   *num*

1. Spell out a number when it begins a sentence:

Five children were playing stickball on Brook Street.
Seventy-five delegates cheered the winning candidate.

If spelling out the number would require three or more words, do not spell it out, but rearrange the sentence so that the number does not come first:

> The winning candidate was cheered by 1,350 delegates.

2. Spell out a number that can be written in one or two words, except as noted in item 4, below:

> The carton will hold four lamps.
> Fifteen hundred spectators watched the ceremony.

3. Use numerals if spelling out a number would require more than two words:

> The number of settlers never exceeded 250,000.

4. Use numerals for addresses, dates, exact times of day, exact sums of money, exact measurements such as miles per hour, scores of games, mathematical ratios, fractions, and page numbers:

> 350 East River Drive   by a score of 108 to 98
> July 4, 1776   a ratio of 3 to 1
> 10:35 A.M.   5/7
> $27.55   page 35
> 55 mph

However, when a time of day or a sum of money is given as a round figure, spell it out:

> The night shift begins at eight o'clock.
> The women were paid ninety cents for fourteen hours of work.
> In those days five dollars was a generous present.

Name_____ Date _____

Exercise 17.   Using Abbreviations and Numbers

Part A.   Each of the following sentences may need an abbreviation and may also include one that is misused. Circle any part of a sentence that includes an error and write the correction in the blank at right. If a sentence is correct as it stands, write *Correct*.

EXAMPLE

(Sen.) Hatfield voted against the appropriation.

Senator

1. For many years, the Federal Bureau of Investigation was dominated by one man—J. Edgar Hoover.   _____

2. Martin Luther King, Junior, first gained national attention by leading a protest march in Selma, Ala.   _____

3. Organic chem. is one of the toughest subjects that a premedical student has to take.   _____

4. Space satellites are launched from Cape Canaveral, Fla.   _____

5. But they are controlled from a tracking station in Houston, Tex.   _____

6. The snake was at least three ft. long.   _____

7. The Rev. Stephen Samuelson gave an inspiring sermon.

_____

8. In Alaska snow covers the ground from Oct. to May.

_____

9. The plane was scheduled to land at 6:45 P.M.

_____

10. Gen. Eisenhower commanded the Allies in World War II.

_____

Part B. In each of the following sentences a number may be written incorrectly. Circle the part of the sentence that includes an error, and write the correction in the blank at right. If a sentence is correct as it stands, write *Correct*.

EXAMPLE

(23) people died in the crash.　　*Twenty-three*　_____

1. Jerry Rubin used to say that he couldn't trust anyone over 30.

_____

2. Shakespeare was born on April twenty-three, fifteen-hundred and sixty-four.

_____

3. Some mechanics are now earning 16 dollars and fifty cents an hour.

_____

4. I got up at 5 o'clock in order to finish my homework.

_____

Name_____ Date _____

Exercise 17, *continued*

5. The snorkel was priced at twenty-eight dollars and ninety-five cents.

_____

6. Many new cars now cost over 10 thousand dollars.

_____

7. The prime minister of England always lives at ten Downing Street.

_____

8. A set of tennis consists of at least six games.

_____

9. 30 minutes after sunset, the sky was coal black.

_____

10. The apples cost 20 cents each.

_____